REVISE GCSE (9–1)

Grammar, Punctuati and Spelling

For English Language and Literature, Humanities, Religious Studies and Science

REVISION WORKBOOK

Author: Cindy Torn

- -

Also available to support your revision:

Revise GCSE Study Skills Guide   9781447967071

The **Revise GCSE Study Skills Guide** is full of tried-and-trusted hints and tips for how to learn more effectively. It gives you techniques to help you achieve your best – throughout your GCSE studies and beyond!

Revise GCSE Revision Planner   9781447967828

The **Revise GCSE Revision Planner** helps you to plan and organise your time, step-by-step, throughout your GCSE revision. Use this book and wall chart to mastermind your revision.

> **For the full range of Pearson revision titles across KS2, KS3, GCSE, Functional Skills, AS/A Level and BTEC visit:**
> www.pearsonschools.co.uk/revise

Contents

ENGLISH FOR EXAMS

1   Standard English
2   Formal & informal language

SPELLING

3   Double letters
4   Silent letters
5   Plurals: adding -s and -es
6   Plurals: words ending in -y
7   Plurals: other endings
8   Irregular plurals
9   Prefixes
10 Suffixes: changes to word endings
11 Suffixes: adding to root words
12 Homophones: contractions
13 Homophones: common groups
14 Common spelling errors
15 'i' before 'e'
16 Spellings for GCSE History
17 Spellings for GCSE Geography
18 Spellings for GSCE Religious Studies
19 Spellings for GCSE Biology
20 Spellings for GCSE Chemistry
21 Spellings for GCSE Physics
22 Spellings for GCSE English Literature
23 Spellings for GSCE English Language

PUNCTUATION

24 Capital letters
25 Sentence endings
26 Commas for extra information
27 Commas in lists
28 Avoiding comma splicing
29 Avoiding other comma errors
30 Colons
31 Semi-colons
32 Brackets and dashes
33 Hyphens
34 Speech marks
35 Contractions
36 Possession: singular
37 Possession: plural

GRAMMAR

38 Articles
39 Different types of pronoun
40 Using pronouns
41 Less or fewer? Who or whom?
42 Whose or who's? That or which?

43 Have or of? Effect or affect?
44 Negatives
45 Active and passive
46 Simple present tense
47 Present continuous tense
48 Simple past tense
49 Irregular past tense
50 The future
51 Modal verbs
52 Subject–verb agreement
53 Tense consistency

STRUCTURING WRITING

54 Paragraphs
55 Introductions
56 Conclusions
57 Conjunctions
58 Useful essay phrases
59 Comparisons
60 Clauses
61 Simple sentences
62 Compound sentences
63 Complex sentences
64 Using quotations
65 Synonyms

EXAM SKILLS

66 Checking your work
67 Correcting errors
68 Improving answers: History
69 Improving answers: Geography
70 Improving answers: Religious Studies
71 Improving answers: Biology
72 Improving answers: Chemistry
73 Improving answers: Physics
74 Improving answers: English Literature
75 Improving answers: English Language

76 Answers

89 Notes

Standard English

Standard English is a form of grammatically correct English that avoids the use of informal language, as well as slang and dialect words.

Don't write how you speak

1 Here are some examples of things people sometimes say. Complete the table below with what you should write instead.

Spoken English (non-Standard)	Written English (Standard)
Me and Danny are going down town.	
I don't want nuthin'.	
That was pretty sick.	
Get in!	
What d'ya want?	

> To make the register of your exam answers more formal, avoid using contractions (such as **don't**), except in creative writing or when quoting directly from a text.

Slang and dialect

2 Replace the slang and dialect expressions in this paragraph with Standard English alternatives.

> Some Russian blokes such as Zubok and Pleshakov have been poking their nose into secret files stashed away in the Soviet Union. These files go on about how bigwigs in Russia during the Cold War were trying to wheedle out of argy-bargy with the USA. This just goes to show that America was the bad guy.

3 Rewrite the following sentences in Standard English.

(a) All right?

....

(b) That exam was a piece of cake.

....

(c) It's reckoned about a third of the people in the world say they're Christian.

....

....

Formal & informal language

There are two main types of register: **formal** and **informal**.

Audience and purpose

1 Circle the correct register for each of these writing purposes.

(a) a text message to a friend	**Formal**	**Informal**
(b) a job application	**Formal**	**Informal**
(c) a letter of complaint to a holiday company	**Formal**	**Informal**
(d) a thank you letter to a relative	**Formal**	**Informal**

Answering exam questions

2 Which exam tip best describes the technique used in each of these sentences? Write the correct numeral in each box.

(a) The Ancient Greeks believed that health was controlled by the four humours: blood, phlegm, yellow bile and black bile. ☐

(b) A microscope is an optical instrument that gives a magnified view of an object. ☐

(c) The economy rapidly fell into recession. ☐

(d) Although there was great loss of life, it could be argued that war led to some of the most significant medical advances of the 20th century. ☐

(i) Use precise vocabulary.

(ii) Use a range of punctuation to vary sentence construction.

(iii) Use subordinating conjunctions at the start of a complex sentence.

(iv) Use concise language that gets to the point.

3 Write a formal equivalent for each of these verbs.

(a) to say sorry ....

(b) to set up ....

(c) to think about ....

4 Rewrite this sentence in a more formal register.

The book writer uses cool language just like me and my mates would use.

....

....

Double letters

When you add a **suffix** to the end of a root word, you sometimes need to double the final letter of the root word.

Adding a suffix to a Consonant–Vowel–Consonant (CVC) root

1 Rewrite these words with the suffix -**ing** added to each.

(a) pad ....

(b) jab ....

(c) shop ....

(d) beg ....

> If a one-syllable root word ends in a CVC pattern, double the final consonant before you add the suffix.

Syllable stress

2 Circle the correct spelling of each of these words.

(a) flattenning / flattening

(b) answerred / answered

(c) omitted / omited

(d) regretted / regreted

(e) happenning / happening

(f) referring / refering

> If the root word has more than one syllable, decide which syllable is stressed. If the stress falls on the first (or penultimate) syllable, do not double the final consonant. If the stress falls on the last syllable, double the final consonant.

3 Rewrite these sentences, adding the correct suffixes (-**ed** or -**ing**) to the verbs in brackets.

(a) He [enter] the house.

....

(b) We'll be [open] the new department next week.

....

(c) She [rebel] against the establishment.

....

(d) Tell me what is [upset] you.

....

(e) [Straighten] his back, he moved from the chair.

....

Silent letters

Some words are tricky to spell because they contain letters that are not sounded out at all. Other words contain letters that are unstressed, which means they are not pronounced how they are spelt.

Silent consonants

1 Circle the silent consonant in each of these words.

    (a) sword   (b) womb   (c) nestle   (d) mortgage   (e) knapsack

    (f) ascend   (g) would   (h) chaos   (i) aisle   (j) wriggle

> **Guided**

Unstressed vowels

2 Circle the unstressed vowel sound in each of these words. The first one has been done for you.

    (a) sep(a)rate   (b) generally

    (c) family   (d) definitely

    (e) colonel   (f) business

    (g) colleague   (h) interesting

    (i) company

> It is easy to misspell a word with an unstressed vowel because it either sounds as if it is not there or makes an **uh** sound, no matter which vowel it is.

3 Complete these words with the correct missing vowels.

    (a) w ___ men   (b) secr ___ t

    (c) calend ___ r   (d) w ___ rdsearch

    (e) w ___ rk   (f) doll ___ r

Plurals: adding -s and -es

To make most nouns **plural**, you simply add **-s**. However, if the singular noun ends in 's', 'x', 'z', 'ch' or 'sh', you add **-es**.

1   Rewrite these words in the plural form.

(a) church   ....   (b) novel   ....

(c) image   ....   (d) wish   ....

(e) cell   ....   (f) suffix   ....

(g) historian   ....   (h) chemical   ....

> Never add apostrophe 's' to make a noun plural. Apostrophes are only used to show possession or where letters are missing.

2   Circle the correct plural forms of the nouns in these sentences.

(a) Viruss / Viruses can infect all living things.

(b) At this time, people refused to pay their taxs / taxes.

(c) The townes / towns were built on river estuaries.

(d) The library contained many rare and valuable books / bookes.

(e) Liam washed the dishs / dishes under protest.

(f) The extraction processs / processes are quite complicated.

3   Tick the correct plurals in these sentences. Correct all the incorrect plurals.

(a) The studentes used compasses to find the correct route, as well as mapes and GPS devicees.

(b) The poems and snatchs of songes in the anthology cover a range of subjectes.

(c) Prefixs are added at the beginnings of words to change meaninges.

Plurals: words ending in -y

There are two straightforward rules for making singular nouns ending in **-y** plural.

Vowel before -y

1 Rewrite these words in the plural form.

(a) abbey ....

(b) journey ....

(c) kidney ....

(d) storey ....

(e) essay ....

(f) valley ....

> If the **-y** follows a vowel, add **-s**.

Consonant before -y

2 Rewrite these words in the plural form.

(a) colony ....

(b) technology ....

(c) army ....

(d) history ....

(e) study ....

(f) enemy ....

> If the **-y** follows a consonant, drop the **-y** and add **-ies**.

3 Circle the correct spelling in each pair of plural words.

(a) babys / babies

(b) screenplays / screenplaies

(c) citys / cities

(d) librarys / libraries

(e) centurys / centuries

(f) holidays / holidaies

(g) supplys / supplies

(h) causeways / causewaies

4 Write a sentence or a short paragraph that includes the plural form of three of these words.

| allergy | alley | army | delay | railway |

| quay | story | gully | victory |

....

....

....

....

Plurals: other endings

There are also rules for the plurals of nouns ending in letters other than **-y**.

> **Guided**

Nouns ending in -o

1   Circle all of the words that need **-es** adding to make them plural. One example has been done for you.

potato	kilo	volcano	cello
solo	studio	hero	zoo
photo	inferno	embargo	tomato
avocado	embryo	stereo	mosquito

> Where there is a vowel directly before the final **-o**, you always just add **-s**.

> **Guided**

2   Write a word ending in **-o** that is correct in the plural whether you add **-s** or **-es**. An example has been given.

cargo(e)s ....

Nouns ending in -f or -fe

3   Rewrite these sentences with the words in brackets in their plural forms.

(a)   The [chef] used [knife].

    ....

(b)   The [wharf] contained [loaf] for distribution.

    ....

(c)   The [thief] have raided all the [safe] in the bank.

    ....

4   Rewrite these words in the plural form.

(a) chief ....   (b) shelf ....

(c) gulf ....   (d) leaf ....

(e) calf ....   (f) belief ....

> To help decide which plural form to use, say the word out loud in a sentence using both forms. Which sounds right?

7

Irregular plurals

Some nouns have an **irregular** plural form, which means they don't follow the rules covered on pages 5–7.

Unmarked plurals

1   Circle the eight nouns that have the same singular and plural forms.

(a) fish	(b) cow	(c) aircraft	(d) Sioux	(e) crisis
(f) headquarters	(g) offspring	(h) haddock	(i) species	(j) appendix
(k) index	(l) series			

> Use a dictionary if you are unsure of any of the plurals.

2   Which of the words you circled in Question 1 is the odd one out? Explain why.

....

....

Other common irregular plurals

3   Circle the correct plural form in each pair of words. In one of the pairs, both plurals are correct.

(a) axes / axises	(b) criterions / criteria	(c) millenniums / millennia
(d) diseases / diseasies	(e) analyses / analysises	(f) nuclei / nucleuses
(g) formulas / formulae	(h) heroes / heros	(i) halfs / halves
(j) deltas / deltae	(k) lice / louses	(l) tooths / teeth

> There is no golden rule for these spellings, so you will need to learn how to spell each plural word individually.

4   Write the plural form of each of these irregular nouns.

(a) child   ....   (b) woman   ....

(c) bacterium   ....   (d) mouse   ....

(e) crisis   ....   (f) fungus   ....

Prefixes

A **prefix** is a group of letters that is added to the front of a root word to change its meaning.

Negative or opposite meaning

1   Rewrite each of these words, adding the correct prefix from the box below to create a negative or opposite meaning.

| a-   anti-   de-   dis-   il-   in-   ir-   un- |

(a) advantage ....

(b) typical ....

(c) literate ....

(d) affordable ....

(e) believable ....

(f) hero ....

(g) rational ....

(h) clutter ....

Different meanings

2   Look at the words in this table.

(a) In the second column, write the meaning of each prefix.

(b) In the third column, write another word that uses the same prefix.

Word	Prefix meaning	Another word with this prefix
extraordinary		
overcook		
upgrade		
autobiography		
outdo		

3   Add the missing prefixes to the words in these sentences. Choose from the prefixes below.

| mega-   ir-   inter-   non-   un-   de-   hyper-   dis-   co- |

(a) The adults were considered to be ....ruly and ....courteous.

(b) The museum had many ....active exhibits.

(c) The phone contract included only two ....bytes of data.

(d) ....operation between water companies has resulted in enough water to meet demands, despite ....even rainfall.

(e) Symptoms of stress include ....sensitivity to stimuli and ....regular sleep patterns.

Suffixes: changes to word endings

A **suffix** is a group of letters added to the end of a root word. Like with prefixes, adding a suffix can change the meaning of the root word.

> **Guided**

1 (a) Rewrite each of these words using the suffix -**less** (meaning **without**). The first example has been done for you.

thought + less = thoughtless	name + less = ...
use + less = ...	mercy + less = ...

(b) Rewrite each of these words using the suffix -**ify** (meaning **to make** or **to become**).

acid + ify = ...	beauty + ify = ...
dignity + ify = ...	code + ify = ...

(c) Rewrite each of these words using the suffix -**ing** (meaning **action of** or **process of**).

allure + ing = ...	handwrite + ing = ...
die + ing = ...	hurry + ing = ...

2 Write down three spelling rules you needed to use to answer Question 1.

(a) ....

....

(b) ....

....

(c) ....

....

3 Circle the correct spelling in each pair of words.

(a) family + s   familys / families

(b) dispose + able   disposeable / disposable

(c) shape + less   shapeless / shapless

(d) ample + ify   amplify / ampleify

Suffixes: adding to root words

You can add **suffixes** to a **root word** to make new words, or to change the tense of verbs.

Word types

> **Guided**

1   Use the suffixes below to make as many variants on the root word as possible. One has been done for you.

> -ing   -ed   -al   -(t)ion   -(s)ion   -(c)ian   -able

(a) pollute   polluting, polluted, pollution   (b) introduce   ....
     ....

(c) decide   ....   (d) discuss   ....
     ....

(e) politic   .... (f) music   ....
     ....

> Remember you sometimes have to change the end of the root word when adding a suffix.

Tricky endings

2   Circle the word that has the correct suffix in each of these groups.

(a) ambision / ambition / ambican   (b) solution / solucian / solusion

(c) antisotial / antisocial   (d) essencial / essential

(e) available / availible   (f) visable / visible

(g) experience / experiance   (h) importence / importance

3   Correct the spelling of each of these words by changing the suffix.

(a) potencial   ....   (b) offitial   ....

(c) suspician   ....   (d) opticion   ....

4   Use the correct suffix to complete the word that fits each of these definitions.

(a) no longer needed / superfluous   redund ....

(b) a competitor or rival   oppon ....

(c) food or nourishment   nutri ....

(d) a cut made with a scalpel   inci ....

Homophones: contractions

A **homophone** is a word that sounds like another word but is spelled differently and has a different meaning.

1 Draw lines to match each homophone with the correct explanation.

it's	This is a possessive pronoun that means **belonging to it**. It never has an apostrophe.
its	This is a contraction that means **it is**. The apostrophe shows where the letter 'i' has been removed.
they're	This is a possessive pronoun that means **belonging to them**.
their	This is a contraction that means **you are**. The apostrophe shows where the letter 'a' has been removed.
there	This is a contraction that means **they are**. The apostrophe shows where the letter 'a' has been removed.
your	This is a possessive pronoun that means **belonging to you**.
you're	This shows the **place or position of something**.

2 Circle the correct homophone in each pair or group.

(a) "It's / Its time for the storm to do it's / its worst."

(b) "Are you sure your / you're teacher said that your / you're homework was good?"

(c) "They're / their / there is no time to waste. They're / their / there catching us up.

Look – over they're / their / there!"

(d) "Your / You're going to be in trouble. You shouldn't have eaten there / their sandwiches!"

3 Write three sentences of your own using these homophones correctly. Choose two homophones from this box to include in each sentence. Use each homophone only once.

they're	your	you're	there	it's	their

....

....

....

....

....

Homophones: common groups

There are certain groups of **homophones** that are more common than others.

To, too and two

1   Use each of these words in a sentence to show the different meanings of **to**, **too** and **two**.

(a) to   ....

(b) too   ....

(c) two   ....

Other common homophones

2   Draw lines to match each homophone with the correct meaning.

here	This is an adverb that means **by** (indicating direction), or **gone by** (indicating time).
hear	This is an adverb that means **audibly**.
past	This is a verb in the past tense that means **permitted**.
passed	This is a verb that means **listen**.
allowed	This is an adverb that means **in this place**. It indicates position.
aloud	This is a verb in the past tense that means **approved** or **succeeded**.

3   Circle the correct homophone in each pair.

(a) What ails / ales thee, knight at arms?

(b) She was fine until she ate / eight too many cakes.

(c) The altar / alter was positioned in the centre of the church.

(d) The banned / band was banned / band from the tour.

(e) Homework is dew / due on Monday.

(f) It was a laps / lapse in judgement.

(g) In this seen / scene Shakespeare introduces Lady Macbeth.

Common spelling errors

Some words **sound very similar** but have different spellings and meanings. Other words **look similar** but sound different and have different meanings.

Near homophones

1 Circle the correct word in each pair.

(a) We are going to work at are / our house.

(b) We should devise / device a revision method that works for us.

(c) My teacher's advice / advise was to create a timetable.

(d) My sister could not accept / except that I was a better singer than her.

(e) The Romantic poets preceded / proceeded the Liverpool Poets.

(f) She stormed of / off in a rage.

(g) He was quiet / quite quiet / quite and shy.

(h) I don't often loose / lose anything, accept / except for my keys.

> Near homophones are words that sound very similar but have different meanings.

Other common errors

2 Use each of these words in a sentence.

(a) though   ....

....

(b) through   ....

....

(c) thought   ....

....

(d) thorough   ....

....

'i' before 'e'

The letter strings '**ie**' and '**ei**' are very common in English. It is sometimes tricky to know which one to use.

When the sound is 'ee', 'i' before 'e' except after 'c'

1   Add 'ie' or 'ei' to complete these words.

(a)   f _ _ ld   (b)   rec _ _ pt   (c)   br _ _ f   (d)   rec _ _ ve

(e)   sh _ _ ld   (f)   misch _ _ f   (g)   dec _ _ ve   (h)   perc _ _ ve

Exceptions to the rule

2   Use each of these words in a sentence.

(a)   protein ....

....

(b)   seize ....

....

(c)   caffeine ....

....

When the rule doesn't apply

3   (a)   Add 'ie' or 'ei' to complete these words.

     (i)   anc _ _ nt   (ii)   sc _ _ nce   (iii)   effic _ _ nt

   (b)   Why are these words unusual?

....

....

> In some cases, the letter string 'ie' or 'ei' doesn't make the sound **ee**, so you cannot apply the 'i' before 'e' rule.

15

Spellings for GCSE History

Make sure you learn the spellings of subject-specific words that will be useful for your History exams.

1 All the words in the table are spelled **incorrectly**. Cross out each word and write the correct spelling underneath it.

govenment	consequance	interpetation	propoganda
....	....	....	....
persacution	Rosevealt	inhibated	contempary
....	....	....	....
parliment	Bolshavik	abolutionists	Varsalles
....	....	....	....
Maio Te-tung	sufferage		
....	....		

> Once you've attempted each spelling, look up any words you are not sure of in a dictionary or in the Revision Guide.

2 Look through your History notes and find five words that you often spell incorrectly. Use each word in a sentence.

(a) ....

(b) ....

(c) ....

(d) ....

(e) ....

⟩**Guided**⟩ **3** List the words from this page that will be useful to you in other subjects. An example has been done for you.

consequence – Geography, English Language, English Literature, Science

....

....

....

....

Spellings for GCSE Geography

Make sure you learn the spellings of subject-specific words that will be useful for your Geography exams.

1   All the words in the table are spelled **incorrectly**. Cross out each word and write the correct spelling underneath it.

enviroment	hydrolic	cylone	malnorishment
....	....	....	....
tetonic	resevoir	decenterlisation	tunami
....	....	....	....
boime	igneus	gentrofication	precipetation
....	....	....	....
interdependance	conjestion		
....	....		

> Once you've attempted each spelling, look up any words you are not sure of in a dictionary or in the Revision Guide.

2   Look through your Geography notes and find five words that you often spell incorrectly. Use each word in a sentence.

(a) ....

(b) ....

(c) ....

(d) ....

(e) ....

3   Write down five words from the table in Question 1 that you find difficult to spell. Can you identify why you find each word difficult to spell? Write down a technique that will help you to remember the correct spelling.

(a) ....

(b) ....

(c) ....

(d) ....

(e) ....

> You might use a rhyme or mnemonic, look for words you know within the word or break it down into syllables.

Spellings for GCSE Religious Studies

Make sure you learn the spellings of subject-specific words that will be useful for your Religious Studies exams.

1   All the words in the table are spelled **incorrectly**. Cross out each word and write the correct spelling underneath it.

athiest	benavelent	omnisient	monothestic ....
Ucherist	contemparory	synergogue	euthenasia ....
reserected	darma	transendance	Quor'an ....
mitsva	samsra	She'a	

> Once you've attempted each spelling, look up any words you are not sure of in a dictionary or in the Revision Guide.

2   Look through your Religious Studies notes and find five words that you often spell incorrectly. Use each word in a sentence.

(a) ....

(b) ....

(c) ....

(d) ....

(e) ....

3   Write down five words from the table in Question 1 that you find difficult to spell. Can you identify why you find each word difficult to spell? Write down a technique that will help you to remember the correct spelling.

(a) ....

(b) ....

(c) ....

(d) ....

(e) ....

> You might use a rhyme or mnemonic, look for words you know within the word or break it down into syllables.

Spellings for GCSE Biology

Make sure you learn the spellings of subject-specific words that will be useful for your Biology exams.

1   All the words in the table are spelled **incorrectly**. Cross out each word and write the correct spelling underneath it.

photosinthasis	endascope	chlorophil	independant
....	....	....	....
acomodation	electralisis	electralite	heamaglobin
....	....	....	....
brethe (verb)	breth (noun)	alleiles	deficiancey
....	....	....	....
homozygus	hetrozygus	coronery	diaphram
....	....	....	....
anarobic	plack		
....	....		

> Once you've attempted each spelling, look up any words you are not sure of in a dictionary or in the Revision Guide.

2   Look through your Biology notes and find five words that you often spell incorrectly. Use each word in a sentence.

(a) ....

(b) ....

(c) ....

(d) ....

(e) ....

Guided   3   List the words from this page that will be useful to you in other subjects. An example has been done for you.

independent: English Language, English Literature, History
....

....

....

....

....

Spellings for GCSE Chemistry

Make sure you learn the spellings of subject-specific words that will be useful for your Chemistry exams.

1   All the words in the table are spelled **incorrectly**. Cross out each word and write the correct spelling underneath it.

aquious	decolorised	cromotography	covalant
buckminsterfulerane	crystalografy	Avogedro	magnisium
reversable	catylist	mieosis	equilibrum
Le Chataleir's	viscocity	homologus	

> Once you've attempted each spelling, look up any words you are not sure of in a dictionary or in the Revision Guide.

2   Look through your Chemistry notes and find five words that you often spell incorrectly. Use each word in a sentence.

(a) ....

(b) ....

(c) ....

(d) ....

(e) ....

3   Write down five words from the table in Question 1 that you find difficult to spell. Can you identify why you find each word difficult to spell? Write down a technique that will help you to remember the correct spelling.

(a) ....

(b) ....

(c) ....

(d) ....

(e) ....

> You might use a rhyme or mnemonic, look for words you know within the word or break it down into syllables.

Spellings for GCSE Physics

Make sure you learn the spellings of subject-specific words that will be useful for your Physics exams.

1 All the words in the table are spelled **incorrectly**. Cross out each word and write the correct spelling underneath it.

saismic	velossity	osiloscope	longditudinal
....	....	....	....
nuclaer fision	newtron	colomb	inferared
....	....	....	....
imission	efficincy	anamally	translucant
....	....	....	....
inersha	satelitte	disipated	
....	....	....	

> Once you've attempted each spelling, look up any words you are not sure of in a dictionary or in the Revision Guide.

2 Look through your Physics notes and find five words that you often spell incorrectly. Use each word in a sentence.

(a) ....

(b) ....

(c) ....

(d) ....

(e) ....

3 Write down five words from the table in Question 1 that you find difficult to spell. Can you identify why you find each word difficult to spell? Write down a technique that will help you to remember the correct spelling.

(a) ....

(b) ....

(c) ....

(d) ....

(e) ....

> You might use a rhyme or mnemonic, look for words you know within the word or break it down into syllables.

Spellings for GCSE English Literature

Make sure you learn the spellings of subject-specific words that will be useful for your English Literature exams.

1   All the words in the table are spelled **incorrectly**. Cross out each word and write the correct spelling underneath it.

soliliquy	ryme	stanzer	pathatic fallicy
....	....	....	....
allegericol	rhytmn	anthropamorfism	dialog
....	....	....	....
imbic pentemetre	metaphore	euphamism	onomotopoia
....	....	....	....

> Once you've attempted each spelling, look up any words you are not sure of in a dictionary or in the Revision Guide.

2   Look through your English Literature notes and find five words that you often spell incorrectly. Use each word in a sentence.

(a) ....

(b) ....

(c) ....

(d) ....

(e) ....

3   Choose five words from the table in Question 1 that you find difficult to spell. Can you identify why you find each word difficult to spell? Write down a technique that will help you to remember the correct spelling.

(a) ....

(b) ....

(c) ....

(d) ....

(e) ....

> You might use a rhyme or mnemonic, look for words you know within the word or break it down into syllables.

Spellings for GCSE English Language

Make sure you learn the spellings of subject-specific words that will be useful for your English Language exams.

1 All the words in the table are spelled **incorrectly**. Cross out each word and write the correct spelling underneath it.

similie	coloquilism	retorical	hyperbolie
....	....	....	....
infrence	synonim	sibilence	apostrophy
....	....	....	....
elipses	techneqe	cleche	sinthesis
....	....	....	....
biassed	evidance	conveiy	
....	....	....	

> Once you've attempted each spelling, look up any words you are not sure of in a dictionary or in the Revision Guide.

2 Look through your English Language notes and find five words that you often spell incorrectly. Use each word in a sentence.

(a) ....

(b) ....

(c) ....

(d) ....

(e) ....

> **Guided**

3 List the words from this page that will be useful to you in other subjects. An example has been done for you.

technique – English Literature, History, Art, Design & Technology, Sciences
....
....
....
....

Capital letters

Capital letters are used at the start of a sentence and for proper nouns.

First letter in a sentence

1   Correct these sentences, adding capital letters where they are needed.

   (a)   "you are fettered," said Scrooge, trembling. "tell me why?"

   (b)   "bah," said Scrooge. "humbug."

   (c)   "christmas a humbug, uncle!" said Scrooge's nephew. "you don't mean that, I am sure."

Proper nouns

2   Correct the words that need a capital letter.

   (a) sir arthur conan doyle   (b) exeter   (c) worry   (d) simile

   (e) hindu   (f) novel   (g) microscope   (h) easter

3   Rewrite these sentences, adding capital letters where required.

   (a)   'a midsummer night's dream', written by william shakespeare, is a complex tale of magic and mayhem.

   ....

   ....

   (b)   the electromagnetic spectrum is a continuous range of wavelengths.

   ....

   ....

   (c)   it is estimated that julius caesar was born in rome in july 100 bc.

   ....

   ....

   (d)   i think religion can be defined as a set of beliefs concerning the cause, purpose and nature of the universe.

   ....

   ....

Sentence endings

You can end a sentence with a **full stop**, a **question mark** or an **exclamation mark**.

Full stop

1   Write an example of each of these types of sentence.

(a) a sentence that gives a fact

....

(b) a sentence that gives an opinion

....

(c) a sentence that gives a command

....

Question mark

2   Write an example of each of these types of question.

(a) question word

....

(b) question tag

....

(c) inversion

....

Exclamation mark

3   Rewrite these sentences, using exclamation marks appropriately.

(a) The shout of "Gas" in Wilfred Owen's poem takes us to the heart of the battlefield.

....

....

(b) "I can't believe the amount of repeats on TV these days!!!" said Josie.

....

....

(c) We must not be afraid of our exams. We must fight for our results.

....

....

Commas for extra information

One common use of **commas** is to separate extra information from the main part of the sentence.

Commas to separate words or phrases

1 Rewrite these sentences to include the extra information.

Sentence	Extra information
(a) Macbeth seized the crown by foul means.	the murderer of Duncan

....

....

(b) Dawlish Warren is a Blue Flag family resort.   near Exeter and Dawlish

....

....

> Use a comma or pair of commas to separate the extra information from the rest of the sentence.

Commas to separate clauses

2 Rewrite each of these sentences, adding in the correct relative pronoun from this box and commas to separate the clauses.

> which   who   whose

(a) Lady Macbeth persuasion led her husband to kill Duncan fell into madness at the end of the play.

....

....

(b) I thanked my tutor had helped me to work on a revision timetable.

....

(c) Fruit should form part of a daily diet is a source of essential nutrients.

....

Commas in lists

Commas are used to separate **items in a list**. They can be used to separate nouns, verbs and adjectives.

Lists of nouns

1 Correct these sentences by adding commas where they are needed.

(a) I will either bake chocolate cake apple pie or banana cake tonight.

(b) Super fruits are thought to contain antioxidants fibre vitamins and minerals

> Use **and** or **or** before the final item in a list, not a comma.

Lists of verbs or adjectives

2 Correct these sentences by adding commas where they are needed.

(a) This evening I could go swimming play basketball or go to the gym.

(b) At the start of the novel, Scrooge could be described as miserly greedy and full of hate.

3 Correct these sentences by adding commas where they are needed.

(a) Lady Macbeth's disturbed frenzied mood continues throughout this scene.

(b) This is an insightful well-observed essay.

> Use a comma to separate two adjectives of equal weight before a noun.

4 Adding or removing a comma can change the meaning of a sentence. Explain the meaning of these two sentences.

(a) Don't call him stupid!

   ....

(b) Don't call him, stupid!

   ....

27

Avoiding comma splicing

It is easy to make mistakes when joining **main clauses**.

Run-on sentences

1 Rewrite this run-on sentence correctly in the following ways.

> Tropical rainforests and mountainous areas receive more water than they lose this results in a water surplus.

(a) using correct punctuation

....

....

(b) using a conjunction

....

....

> In a run-on sentence, two main clauses follow one another without the correct punctuation or conjunction.

Comma splicing

2 Rewrite this sentence to avoid comma splicing.

> The narrative is third person, the author has used the pronouns **he** and **she**.

....

....

> Comma splicing is when two independent clauses are incorrectly joined with a comma.

3 Correct these sentences to avoid comma splicing using the instructions given in brackets.

(a) We still live in a society where men dominate political spheres, women also have the power to change the policies that constrain us. (Use a conjunction.)

(b) Offenders who leave after a longer time get more help readjusting to normal life, those on shorter sentences don't. (Use a semi-colon.)

(c) I don't really care for science, on the other hand, I'd rather study science than maths. (Create two separate sentences.)

> Make sure you mark your corrections to each sentence clearly.

Avoiding other comma errors

Misuse of commas is common when adding phrases or clauses of extra information to a sentence.

Restrictive phrases

1   Underline the restrictive phrases in these sentences.

     (a)   The girl who copied my work is in the canteen.

     (b)   The car with the chipped paintwork damaged my bicycle.

     (c)   One of the reasons why people in developing countries use water that is polluted with animal and human waste is because they have no other choice due to lack of piped water.

> A restrictive phrase contains information that is essential to the meaning of the sentence.

That and which

2   Which sentence would you use to describe each of these images? Write the letter of the sentence in the box.

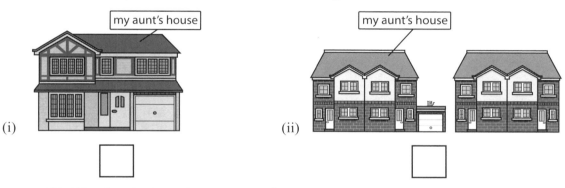

   (i)   [ ]   (ii)   [ ]

   (a)   The house, which has a garage, belongs to my aunt.

   (b)   The house that has a garage belongs to my aunt.

3   What is the difference in meaning between these two sentences?

   (a)   The photograph, which shows a piece of slate, illustrates the formation of metamorphic rock.

   (b)   The photograph that shows a piece of slate illustrates the formation of metamorphic rock.

....

....

....

Colons

A **colon** is used to introduce further information or further explanation to a sentence.

Colons for further information

1   Rewrite these sentences correctly, adding colons and any other punctuation needed.

(a)   For my revision I need the following some sticky notes some highlighter pens and some A4 paper.

....

....

(b)   Macbeth could be described in many ways easily persuaded overly ambitious and murderous.

....

....

(c)   I have two options here continue revising or watch football.

....

....

2   Rewrite one of the sentences in Question 1 as a bullet-pointed list.

....

....

....

....

Colons for further explanation

3   Rewrite these sentences correctly, adding colons and any other punctuation needed.

(a)   these worms are a type of zombie worm they have no eyes or mouth

....

....

(b)   hooke's microscope was not very powerful the glass lenses were of poor quality

....

....

Semi-colons

Semi-colons are used to separate items and to link clauses.

Semi-colons to separate items

1   Rewrite this bullet-pointed list as one sentence, using semi-colons to separate the detailed items.

> In Jane Austen's 'Pride and Prejudice', the Bennet sisters are:
> - Jane, who is beautiful and thoughtful
> - Elizabeth, who is the lively and witty main character of the novel
> - Mary, who is the serious and plain member of the family
> - Catherine or 'Kitty', who is easily led by her younger sister
> - Lydia, who is frivolous, headstrong and thoughtless.

....

....

....

....

....

....

Semi-colons to link clauses

2   Add a semi-colon to each of these sentences to join the clauses correctly.

(a) Simon likes hot curry William won't eat it.

(b) There was nowhere to sit in the library it was not possible to work.

(c) I didn't do my homework I'm now in detention.

3   Write a sentence to show correct use of the semi-colon for each function.

(a) to separate items

....

....

(b) to link clauses

....

....

Brackets and dashes

Brackets and **dashes** can be used to add extra information to a sentence.

Brackets

1   Rewrite these sentences, adding the bracketed information in the correct places.

   (a)   (who discovered radium)
          Marie Curie was a Polish and naturalised-French physicist.

   ....

   ....

   (b)   (rock formations)
          In the Dartmoor National Park you will find ponies, forests and tors.

   ....

   ....

> Bracketed information can go in the middle or at the end of a sentence.

Dashes

2   Add a pair of dashes in the correct places in these sentences.

   (a)   Mr Darcy at first hated by Elizabeth wins her hand in marriage by the end of the novel.

   (b)   Respiration the chemical reaction that releases energy from glucose happens in mitochondria.

> Unlike brackets, you cannot use a pair of dashes at the end of a sentence.

3   Add a single dash in the correct place in each of these sentences.

   (a)   In the kitchen, the rule is simple wash your hands before you start.

   (b)   "I just need to start my revision hey! Is that a football match?"

> A single dash can be used to mark a break between clauses. This is best avoided in formal writing.

4   Rewrite this sentence, adding a set of dashes and a set of brackets.

   Mitochondria found in the cytoplasm make most of the cell's supply of ATP
   adenosine triphosphate.

   ....

   ....

Hyphens

A **hyphen** is a short, straight line used to join words.

1 Draw lines to match each function of a hyphen with the correct example.

Functions of hyphens	Examples
to make some compound adjectives	well-being
to make some compound nouns	self-confident
to make some compound verbs	seventy-three
to make compound numbers	semi-industrial
to add a prefix ending with a vowel to a word starting with a vowel	to sound-proof
with other prefixes, especially before capital letters	un-American

2 (a) Add a hyphen to this sentence in the appropriate position.

The government is offering a grant to small business owners.

   (b) Why is the hyphen needed?

   ....

   ....

3 Correct these sentences by adding hyphens where they are needed.

   (a) My brother and my sister in law have a six year old daughter.

   (b) Over the counter medicines are also known as non prescription medicines.

   (c) The ex chair of the football club used up to date training methods.

Speech marks

Speech marks are used to show the exact words that someone says. They are also known as inverted commas or quotation marks.

Direct speech

1 Correct these sentences by adding speech marks and any other punctuation that is needed.

(a) I thought it was madness he said, as he replaced the obnoxious paper in the safe, and now I begin to fear it is disgrace.

(b) If anyone knows, it will be Lanyon he had thought.

(c) I suppose, Lanyon said he you and I must be the two oldest friends that Henry Jekyll has?

Indirect speech

2 These sentences are examples of indirect speech. Rewrite them so that they are examples of direct speech.

(a) Enfield said that at about three a.m. on a black winter morning he had felt very uneasy.

....

....

(b) The doctor said that it was such unscientific balderdash.

....

....

(c) He inquired whether this Mr. Hyde was a person of small stature.

....

....

3 Explain the meaning of the term **reporting clause**.

....

....

Contractions

Contractions are made by joining two words together into one shortened form. They are useful for making speech sound more natural in creative writing.

Apostrophe placement

1 (a) On the first answer line, rewrite each contraction, moving the apostrophe to the correct place.

   (b) On the second answer line, write the two words that have been joined.

      (i)   your'e   ....

      (ii) its'   ....

      (iii) wer'e   ....

      (iv) wo'nt   ....

      (v)   wouldv'e   ....

      (vi) had'nt   ....

      (vii) theyl'l   ....

      (viii) theyr'e   ....

2 When is it acceptable to use contractions in your exam?

....

....

Common contractions

3 Rewrite these sentences using contractions.

   (a) You must not use contractions in formal writing.

....

   (b) I shall not miss the pressure of examinations.

....

   (c) What are you doing this weekend?

....

   (d) He is a talented player.

....

Possession: singular

An **apostrophe** can be used to show that something belongs to someone or something else.

Singular nouns

1   Rewrite each of these phrases, using an apostrophe + **-s** to show possession.

(a) the opinion of the girl ....

(b) the approaches of the city ....

(c) the focus of China ....

(d) the power of the metaphor ....

(e) the wealth of the nation ....

Singular nouns ending in 's'

2   Circle the word with the apostrophe in the correct place in each pair of phrases.

(a) Thomas's / Thoma's bike   (b) the duchess' / duchess's retinue

(c) the rhinocero's / rhinoceros's habitat   (d) Texas's / Texas' landscape

3   Rewrite each of these sentences, using a possessive apostrophe instead of the word **of**.

(a) The Primary School of St James is closing after 100 years.

....

(b) The main use of a scatter graph is to identify a relationship between two variables.

....

(c) The itinerary of the river cruise includes visits to local heritage sites.

....

(d) The spines of a cactus protect it from being eaten and help to reduce water loss.

....

(e) Putting these antigens into the body of a child causes an immune response.

....

Possession: plural

An **apostrophe** can also be used to show when something belongs to more than one person or thing (a plural noun).

Plurals ending in 's'

1   Rewrite each of these phrases, using an apostrophe to show possession.

(a)   the characters of the plays   ....

(b)   the howls of the dogs   ....

(c)   the themes of the novels   ....

Irregular plurals

2   Rewrite each of these phrases, using apostrophe + -**s** to show possession.

(a)   the toys belonging to the children   ....

(b)   the rights of the people   ....

(c)   the barn of the oxen   ....

3   Correct these sentences by adding the missing apostrophes to the plural nouns.

(a)   The geeses nests were flooded by unusually heavy rainfall.

(b)   Bacterias main role in the digestive system is to help break down undigested food.

4   (a)   Correct these singular and plural possessive noun phrases by adding the missing apostrophes.

(b)   Write **S** or **P** next to each phrase below to show whether the noun is singular or plural.

(i)   the classes books   ☐   (ii)   the sheeps fleeces   ☐

(iii)   Carloss football boots   ☐   (iv)   Loiss ballet class   ☐

(c)   The nouns in examples (v) and (vi) below could be either singular or plural, depending on the position of the apostrophe. Write both alternatives for each noun and state which is singular (S) and which is plural (P).

(v)   the teachers suggestions   (vi)   the parents evening

.... ☐   .... ☐

.... ☐   .... ☐

Articles

An **article** is a type of determiner you put at the start of a noun phrase to make it either specific or general.

Definite and indefinite articles

1   Add the correct indefinite article (**a** or **an**) before each of these words.

(a) ....crystal   (b) ....war   (c) ....electrode   (d) ....hour

(e) ....eulogy   (f) ....university   (g) ....hospital   (h) ....ambush

> Use **a** when the word starts with a consonant or 'u' or 'eu' if it makes the sound **you**. Use **an** when the word starts with a vowel (a, e, i, o, u) or a silent 'h'.

2   Explain the difference in meaning between the two phrases in each pair.

(a)   a girl over there   the girl over there

....

....

(b)   an Anglo-Saxon punishment   the Anglo-Saxon punishment

....

....

Common mistakes

3   Rewrite these sentences using the correct determiners.

(a)   Alot of an prisoners suffered from poor health due to a dirty conditions.

....

....

(b)   An hyperbole is the exaggeration.

....

....

(c)   Them cells with one copy of each chromosome are haploid.

....

....

Different types of pronoun

There are three different types of **pronouns**: personal pronouns, possessive pronouns and relative pronouns.

Personal pronouns

1   Correct these sentences by replacing the repeated nouns with the correct pronouns.

(a)   The writer uses imagery to symbolise terror. The writer also uses sounds that reflect her fear.

(b)   There were many reasons why Germany opposed the Treaty of Versailles. Firstly, the Treaty of Versailles was seen as a Diktat.

(c)   The artists used the surrounding environment for their work. The artists did not want to merely show the landscape; instead, the artists wanted to capture the spirit of the landscape.

Possessive pronouns

2   Use at least three possessive pronouns from this table in a sentence of your own.

with a noun	my	your	his/her/its	our	their
instead of a noun	mine	yours	his/her/its	ours	theirs

....

....

....

Relative pronouns (who, whose, that, which)

3   Circle the relative pronoun and underline the relative clause in each of these sentences.

(a)   Elizabeth Bennet, who delighted in nonsense, found Mr Collins ridiculous.

(b)   1907 saw the official introduction of probation officers, whose job was to check on offenders living outside prison.

(c)   The infantry, which was becoming more significant, embraced the invention of rifles.

Using pronouns

Using **pronouns** correctly will make your writing clear and grammatically correct.

Too many pronouns

1   Underline the pronouns in these sentences. Then, explain why they make each sentence difficult to understand.

(a) Will and Jim ran back to his house because he had left his PE kit in his room.

....

....

(b) Increasing frequency of storms and periods of hot, dry weather are both examples of weather experienced in the UK. This can increase the risk of flooding.

....

....

(c) It flows naturally from side to side, around ridges in the valley sides called spurs.

....

....

Its and it's

2   Circle the correct form of **its/it's** in each pair.

(a) It's / Its the process of repeatedly undercutting and collapsing that causes the formation of a steep-sided gorge.

(b) When the river is small, it's / its energy is limited.

(c) It's / Its response is large and rapid because an extensive amount of antibodies is produced very quickly.

> Remember **its** with no apostrophe is a possessive pronoun; **it's** with an apostrophe is a contraction of two words: **it** and **is**.

Me, myself and I

3   Circle the correct pronoun to complete each of these sentences.

(a) The teacher gave the homework back to I / me / myself.

(b) I bought a birthday present for I / me / myself.

(c) My brother and I / me / myself went for a run.

Less or fewer? Who or whom?

Mixing up **less** with **fewer** and **who** with **whom** are common mistakes that you should avoid in your exam writing.

Less or fewer?

1   Add **less** or **fewer** before each word or phrase.

(a) .... laws   (b) .... oppression   (c) .... money

(d) .... opportunities (e) .... than a mile   (f) .... rain

(g) .... clean air   (h) .... diseases   (i) .... than £50

2   Tick the sentences in which **less** and **fewer** have been used correctly. Correct the sentences in which they have been used incorrectly.

(a) Children had fewer chance of a
good education.   ☐

(b) Fewer children went to school.   ☐

(c) Less workers were joining
the unions.   ☐

(d) There was less food to go round.   ☐

Who or whom?

3   Complete each sentence by writing **who** or **whom** in the gap.

(a) .... would like to leave early?

(b) To .... it may concern.

(c) The police arrested 50 demonstrators, most of .... were later released.

4   Rewrite these informal sentences as formal sentences using **whom**.

(a) Who should I send my CV to?

....

(b) Who did Elizabeth visit Pemberley with?

....

Whose or who's? That or which?

In addition to **who** and **whom**, it is common to make mistakes with other relative pronouns.

Whose or who's?

1   Circle the correct form of **who's/whose** in each sentence.

   (a) The local people, who's / whose wages were very low, could not afford to buy houses in the valley.

   (b) Our uncle, who's / whose very sporty, loves to go swimming.

   (c) Who's / Whose got the power to declare war?

   (d) The service is for people who's / whose lives have been disrupted by war.

> Remember to avoid contractions in exam writing.

That or which?

2   Complete these sentences by writing **that** or **which** in the gaps. Add in any missing punctuation.

   (a) The train .... doesn't run on Sunday, is free to visitors all season.

   (b) The glacier .... lies above the Chamonix is retreating rapidly.

   (c) Football .... many of us enjoy, is a very skilful sport.

   (d) This is the film .... everyone is talking about.

> A clause that isn't essential to the sentence (a non-restrictive clause) must begin with **which** and be separated from the main sentence by a pair of commas.

3   Complete these sentences by writing **who's**, **whose**, **that** or **which** in the gaps.

   (a) Piggy, ... real name is never revealed, is the most vulnerable member of the group.

   (b) It bounces off the table and hits my headteacher, ... looking straight at me.

   (c) The mountains .... are found in the Chamonix valley are the highest in the Alps

   (d) Skiing, ... is my favourite sport, can be very expensive.

Have or of? Effect or affect?

Mixing up **have** with **of** and **effect** with **affect** are common mistakes you should avoid.

Always use could have, not could of

1   Rewrite these sentences, ensuring they are appropriate for exam writing.

(a)   Henry VIII could of wanted to impress Francis I.

....

(b)   Richard I's companions might of described him as a fearless warrior.

....

Effect and affect

2   Complete these sentences by writing the correct forms of **effect** or **affect** in the gaps.

(a)   Research shows that the amount of sleep you have .... your exam grades.

(b)   Weather conditions have an .... on residents in the south-west.

(c)   The beneficial .... of drinking water are well-known.

> Remember that **effect** is a noun and **affect** is a verb.

3   Rewrite these sentences, ensuring they are appropriate for exam writing.

(a)   I could of improved if I'd of known the long-term affects of my actions.

....

....

(b)   An early football injury might of effected his mobility.

....

....

(c)   I should of volunteered for the study into the affects of revision on exam results.

....

....

Negatives

It is important that you use the correct **negative** forms in your exam writing.

Avoid double negatives

1   Correct the double negatives in these sentences.

   (a) Thomas Sydenham convinced people that a disease didn't have nothing to do with the person who had it.

   (b) Most Exodusters didn't have no money for setting up a farm.

   (c) The big ranchers would not share none of their political power with the newcomers.

Doesn't, don't and ain't

2   Complete these sentences by adding **doesn't** or **don't** in the gaps.

   (a) She .... want to go to revision club.

   (b) Draw clearly, but .... worry about creating a work of art!

   (c) One advantage of developing wind energy is that it .... pollute the atmosphere with harmful greenhouse gases.

3   Rewrite these sentences, replacing **ain't** and any double negatives with the correct negative forms.

   (a) Elizabeth's family ain't got much money so she can't buy no fine clothes.

   ....

   (b) Piggy is intellectual but he ain't got no common sense.

   ....

   (c) There ain't a single member of the family who ain't implicated in Eva's demise.

   ....

Active and passive

You can write a clause in either the **active** or the **passive** voice.

Active voice

1 Rewrite these passive sentences in the active voice.

(a) | The window was broken by me.

....

(b) | The chocolate was eaten by William.

....

Passive voice

2 The subject of the verb is not known in these active sentences. Rewrite the sentences in the passive voice.

(a) | ? delivered three letters this morning.

....

(b) | ? put the test tube in the rack.

....

Using the active and passive

3 (a) Identify whether these sentences are in the active or the passive voice. Circle the answers.

   (i) Unruly students roam the corridors.   **Active**   **Passive**

   (ii) The flask filled with water was held in place by the clamp.   **Active**   **Passive**

   (iii) The last cake was eaten by whom?   **Active**   **Passive**

(b) Rewrite each sentence from Question 3(a) in the other voice.

   (i) ....

   (ii) ....

   (iii) ....

Had a go ☐ Nearly there ☐ Nailed it! ☐

Simple present tense

You use the **simple present tense** to talk about something that is happening in the present, something that is currently or always the case, or something that happens regularly.

Examples of the simple present tense

1   Tick the sentences that are in the simple present tense.

(a)   Matthew eats pizza regularly. ☐

(b)   Elizabeth I reigned over England from 1558. ☐

(c)   Prince Charles is heir to the throne. ☐

(d)   My family knows how to ski. ☐

(e)   The dog jumped up onto the wall. ☐

(f)   The headteacher speaks for the governing body. ☐

(g)   I spoke to my tutor about revision. ☐

(h)   The Tet Offensive was launched at the start of 1968. ☐

(i)   The poet describes the landscape as intimidating. ☐

(j)   There are running clubs in the area if you wish to take up this sport. ☐

(k)   Stalin died and Khrushchev became the Soviet leader. ☐

Regular and irregular verbs

2   Complete the table to show the simple present tense forms of the verbs **to talk, to be** and **to have**.

	to talk	to be	to have
I			
you (singular)			
he/she/it			
we			
you (plural)			
they			

3   These verb phrases are in the simple past tense. Rewrite them in the **simple present tense**.

(a)   you were   ....

(b)   she walked   ....

(c)   I broke   ....

(d)   she built   ....

(e)   they bought ....

(f)   he caught   ....

(g)   I crept   ....

(h)   we drove   ....

Present continuous tense

The **present continuous tense** is used to talk about events that are still in progress at the time of writing. The **past continuous tense** is used to talk about ongoing events in the past.

Present continuous tense

1   Complete this table to show the present continuous forms of the verb **to write**.

Simple present	Present continuous (<u>to be</u> plus -ing)
I write	
you write (singular)	
he/she/it writes	
we write	
you write (plural)	
they write	

> **Guided** >

2   Complete these present continuous verb phrases.

(a) to panic

I ....am panicking.........................

(b) to vote

she ....

(c) to agree

he ....

(d) to stop

you ....

Past continuous tense

3   Complete the table to show the past continuous forms of the verb **to read**.

Simple present	Past continuous (<u>to be</u> plus -ing)
I read	
you read (singular)	
he/she/it reads	
we read	
you read (plural)	
they read	

4   Complete these past continuous verb phrases.

(a) to put

we ....

(b) to dance

they ....

(c) to go

you ....

(d) to save

we ....

Simple past tense

You can use the **simple past tense** to talk about an event that has already happened.

Single-syllable verbs

1   Write the simple past tense forms of these verbs.

(a) add ....

(b) beg ....

(c) file ....

(d) play ....

(e) spy ....

(f) hope ....

2   (a)   This table shows the rules for adding **-ed** to single-syllable verbs. Draw lines to match each verb ending to the correct rule.

(b)   Complete the table with an example of each verb type.

Verb...
ending with two or more consonants.
with a short vowel sound and ending with one consonant.
ending with an 'e'.
ending with a consonant and a 'y'.
ending with a vowel and a 'y'.

Rule	Example
Double the consonant and add **-ed**.	
Add **-d**.	
Do not change the 'y' to an 'i'. Simply add **-ed**.	
Add **-ed**.	
Change the 'y' to an 'i' and add **-ed**.	

Multi-syllable verbs ending Vowel–Consonant

3   Write the simple past tense forms of these verbs.

(a) prefer ....

(b) occur ....

(c) emit ....

(d) label ....

(e) travel ....

(f) worship ....

(g) kidnap ....

(h) develop ....

(i) finish ....

(j) complete ....

> Watch out for the two that don't fit the Vowel–Consonant rule for multi-syllable verbs.

Irregular past tense

Some verbs are irregular in their past tense forms.

1 (a) Complete each word in the second column to give the simple past form of each verb.

(b) Write an example sentence using each verb in the simple past tense.

Verb	Simple past form	Example sentence
to be	w _ _ or _ _ r _	....
to go	_ _ _ t	....
to take	t _ _ _	....
to see	_ a _	....
to give	g _ _ _	....
to show	_ h _ _ _ _	....
to begin	b _ _ _ _	....
to write	_ _ _ _ e	....
to speak	_ p _ _ _	....
to do	_ _ _	....

> **Guided**

2 Write a sentence in the present perfect tense using the past participle of each of these verbs.

(a) to choose <u>I have chosen my college courses for next year.</u> ....

(b) to wear ....

(c) to steal ....

(d) to revise ....

(e) to go ....

The future

There is no separate future tense, but there are many ways of using the present tense to speak about the future.

Going to

1 Rewrite each of these sentences to talk about future events, using the present tense of the verb <u>to be</u> + **going to**.

(a) I completed my revision timetable.

....

(b) The size of the school has grown from 800 students to 1000 students.

....

Will

2 Rewrite each of these sentences to talk about future events, using the modal verb **will** followed by another verb.

(a) This meant that switching troops from one front to another quickly was essential.

....

(b) Uniting the nation requires a single leader.

....

Using other verbs to talk about the future

3 (a) Now choose one of the sentences in Question 2 and rewrite it using a modal verb such as **should** or **might**.

....

(b) How has the meaning changed?

....

....

Present tense for the future

4 Rewrite this sentence to talk about future events, using a present tense verb.

I sat my Maths exam on Thursday.

....

To make it clearer that you are talking about the future, change the time expression **on Thursday** to something more appropriate.

Modal verbs

A **modal verb** is a type of auxiliary verb. This means that it comes before another verb and changes the meaning of that second verb.

Possibility, ability and necessity

1   Sort these modal verbs into the table according to their functions.

may	will	might	must	should	ought to
can	could	shall	would	have to	need to

> Two of the words have more than one function, so they will appear in two of the columns.

Possibility	Ability	Necessity

2   Sort the modal verbs from the box in Question 1 into this table according to whether they suggest high or low degrees of certainty.

Certain	Less certain

3   You may find these modal verb contractions in older literary texts. Rewrite them in their uncontracted form.

(a) I shan't ....   (b) I oughtn't ....

(c) I mayn't ....

4   Add an appropriate modal verb to each of these sentences.

(a) Stalin had two options in 1939: he .... have maintained the friendship with France or negotiated with Germany.

(b) Meena broke her leg and .... spend several months in hospital.

(c) The harvest has been poor and there .... not be enough food to last the winter.

Subject–verb agreement

The **verb** you use must always agree with its **subject**.

Singular or plural noun

1   Rewrite each of these sentences, changing the subject from singular to plural and changing the rest of the sentence to agree with it.

(a)   Mass movement is the downhill movement of material under the influence of gravity.

....

....

(b)   The team is made up of mixed-age students.

....

....

> Make sure the verb agrees with the subject!

More than one subject

2   Circle the correct verb forms in these sentences.

(a)   The River Lugg and the River Wye has / have formed the landscape of Hereford and Worcester.

(b)   Onomatopoeia and assonance create / creates a sense of the battlefield.

(c)   The teacher or a teaching assistant are / is in the classroom at all times.

Noun phrases

3   Add the missing forms of <u>to be</u> to this sentence.

> Igneous rock, including granite and basalt, ... hard and formed of crystals, so it .... resistant to erosion.

Collective nouns

4   Circle the correct verb forms in these sentences.

(a)   The police is / are concerned about public safety in the area.

(b)   The children go / goes to the local school.

(c)   The army has / have been given the orders.

(d)   The football team is / are playing against its bitterest rivals on Sunday.

> Collective nouns should be singular, except for **police**, which is always plural.

Tense consistency

In your writing, you should choose an appropriate tense and stick to it.

Past tense

1   Correct this passage about Hippocrates so that the tense is consistently in the past.

> Hippocrates is an Ancient Greek doctor. His ideas and books are very influential well
>
> into medieval times and beyond. He dismisses the idea that gods cause disease – he
>
> believes that there is a physical reason for illness, which needs a physical cure.

> In subjects such as History, you should describe events using the past tense.

Present tense

2   Circle the correct verbs in each of these sentences so that the tense is consistently in the present.

(a)   The first line suggested / suggests that Manderley is / was an important place as the narrator had / has 'dreamt' of it 'again'.

(b)   Both writers begin / began by trying to encourage their audiences to support the viewpoints they offered / offer.

(c)   Campaigners for restorative justice programmes claimed / claim it can reduce reoffending by up to 27%.

> In English Literature, you use the present tense to describe characters and their actions. In English Language, you use it to analyse how a writer uses language and structure.

3   Correct the inconsistent tenses in the short story extract below.

> I don't think I am ever as scared as when I watched my first scary movie when I am only
>
> 7 years old. It is 7 o'clock and it becomes dark outside. My mum was in the same room
>
> as me, but she is doing the ironing.
>
> I switched on the TV and I am pressing play. I watch in silence, until it will get to the
>
> very end.

Paragraphs

Use **paragraphs** to present your writing in an organised, logical way and to help you gain high marks for SPaG.

Using TiPToP

1 (a) Insert double slashes (//) to mark where you would start new paragraphs in these extracts. You may need to insert more than one double slash per extract.

(b) Using TiPToP, explain why you decided to start a new paragraph in each case.

(i) The 1830 Indian Removal Act forced Indians in eastern states to move west of the Mississippi River. The US government forced 46,000 eastern Indians to give up their lands in return for new lands west of the Mississippi River. Whites then thought this land was worthless – the 'Great American Desert'. In 1834 the Indian Trade and Intercourse Act set out the frontier between the USA and Indian Territory.

> You can use **TiPToP** to help you remember to start a new paragraph when the **Ti**me, **P**erson, **To**pic or **P**lace changes.

Reason: ....

(ii) The government needed US citizens to go and live in its new territories in the West. By the 1850s, white Americans wanted to use parts of the lands in the West that had been given to Indians. Reservations were the solution.

Reason: ....

(iii) Hard rocks like chalk are often left jutting out in the sea, forming headlands. Soft rocks such as sands are eroded more quickly, forming bays. Cliffs are common coastal features. Cliffs are shaped through weathering and erosion.

Reason: ....

(iv) "We have common friends," said Mr Utterson. "Common friends!" echoed Mr Hyde, a little hoarsely. "Who are they?" "Jekyll, for instance," said the lawyer. "He never told you," cried Mr Hyde, with a flush of anger. "I did not think you would have lied." "Come," said Mr Utterson, "that is not fitting language."

Reason: ....

Introductions

An **introduction** needs to engage the reader and set the tone for your writing.

Writing to present a viewpoint

Guided

1 Look at these opening sentences from writing to present a viewpoint tasks. Identify the technique that the writer uses in each introduction. An example has been done for you.

(a)
> Over 5 million children under 10 have a social media account.

Starting with a surprising or shocking fact or statistic
....

(b)
> How many hours a week do you think that you spend on your mobile phone?

....

(c)
> Talent shows merely encourage ruthless competition and they allow the talentless to make fools of themselves.

....

(d)
> Although I knew that villages on the edge of the UK coastline were disappearing, I had no idea that I would soon witness the devastation at first hand.

....

(e)
> "I believe that unarmed truth and unconditional love will have the final word."
> Martin Luther King.

....

Imaginative writing

2 Draw a line to match each idea with the correct example.

Idea	Example
Start with a vivid description. Use a mix of senses to evoke the setting.	We rely on our senses for survival. But we are not beasts. We have culture. Yet we cannot ignore our instincts. And those instincts mean we always win.
Start with interesting dialogue. Use interesting verbs and adverbs to make your reader infer what the characters might be talking about.	The smell of over-boiled swede and cabbage hit him as he entered the school canteen. A sea of black school blazers met his wary gaze.
Start with a sense of mystery, conflict or danger. Leave the reader guessing (the exact setting is not described) and reveal the mystery slowly.	"Are you certain?" she asked as she moved silently towards the door. "No. I'm never certain," he whispered. "The dawn will show us the truth."

Conclusions

Make sure you plan how you are going to finish your piece of writing before you start.

Writing to present a viewpoint

1   Write a final sentence using the technique suggested for each of these pieces of writing.

   (a)   An article persuading older people to use the internet (End with an image).

      ....

      ....

   (b)   An article giving your opinion on school uniform (End with a question).

      ....

      ....

   (c)   A letter giving your opinion on using animals in circuses (End with a warning).

      ....

      ....

   (d)   An article persuading the Government to allow young people to drive at age 16 (End with a call to action).

      ....

      ....

Imaginative writing

2   Look at these ideas for achieving a strong ending to a piece of imaginative writing. Decide which three should be followed and which three should be avoided. Circle your choices.

   (a)   Plan the tone of your ending in advance.   **Follow**   **Avoid**

   (b)   Change the mood suddenly.   **Follow**   **Avoid**

   (c)   Use an ending you know already or a sudden twist.   **Follow**   **Avoid**

   (d)   Give your final sentence impact.   **Follow**   **Avoid**

   (e)   Try a long ending.   **Follow**   **Avoid**

   (f)   Make sure your writing reaches a resolution.   **Follow**   **Avoid**

Conjunctions

Conjunctions link words, phrases or clauses together.

Using conjunctions in your writing

1 (a) Sort these conjunctions into the table. There are three conjunctions for each purpose.

accordingly	also	besides	following this	formerly
hitherto	in brief	in conclusion	in the same way	likewise
on the contrary	such as	to illustrate this	to summarise	undeniably

(b) Think of one or more additional conjunctions for each purpose. Add them to the table.

Purpose	Examples of conjunctions
Adding to and explaining a point	
Illustrating and emphasising a point	
Comparing and contrasting	
Showing time	
Summarising and making judgements	

2 Complete this passage using the conjunctions from the box.

although	firstly	for example	furthermore	including

................................, medical staff working with radioactive sources have their

exposure limited in a number of ways, ... increasing their distance

from the source, shielding the source and minimising the time they spend in the

presence of sources. ...., their exposure is closely monitored using

dosimeter badges. .... some patients may be exposed to a dose

of radiation for medical diagnosis or treatment (................................, detecting and

treating cancer), this is only done when the benefits are greater than the possible harm.

Useful essay phrases

Carefully chosen **essay phrases** can improve your written answers significantly.

1 (a) Sort these useful essay phrases into the table according to their purpose. There are two phrases for each purpose.

> on the other hand   for this reason   having said that   this suggests that
> all things considered   this makes it clear that   of central concern is
> to put it another way   the dominant theme is   to say nothing of

(b) Think of one or more additional useful essay phrases for each purpose. Add them to the table.

Purpose	Examples of phrases
Adding and explaining a point	
Explaining further	
Illustrating and emphasising a point	
Comparing and contrasting	
Summarising and making judgements	

2   Complete this passage using the useful essay phrases from the box.

> this meant that   despite this   with this in mind   it has been established that

.... there is not enough ethnic diversity in football coaching in the UK. In 2014, a group of former and current footballers announced that football should aim to employ at least one manager from a BAME background for every five positions in the top league. .... there needed to be an increase of almost 600% (from 3.4%). ...., footballing authorities suggested a number of measures and incentives to increase this figure. ...., the figure had increased by just 20% in the two years following.

Comparisons

When you want to compare one thing to another or to a group, you can use a **comparative** or a **superlative** adjective.

Comparatives

1 Tick the correct comparatives in these sentences. Correct all the incorrect comparatives.

(a) When the temperature is more cool, more of the Earth is covered in ice. This is called a glacial. When the Earth is warmer, like now, it is called an interglacial.

(b) Because of global warming, extreme weather is frequenter: heat extremes are five times more common than 100 years ago.

(c) Caffeine and chocolate are more likely to lead to headaches than nutritiouser snacks such as fresh fruit and water.

(d) It is clearly beneficialer to use brownfield sites because they are less damaging to the environment.

Superlatives

2 Next to each adjective, write the comparative form (**more** or **-er**) and the superlative form (**most** or **-est**).

(a) tangled   ....

(b) sad   ....

(c) important   ....

(d) far   ....

> Watch out for the irregular adjective!

Irregular comparatives and superlatives

3 Complete this table.

Adjective	Comparative	Superlative
little		
much		
good		
many		

Clauses

A **main clause** makes a complete sentence, while a **subordinate clause** or **relative clause** needs to be added to a main clause to make a complete sentence.

Main clauses

1   Circle the subject and underline the verb in each of these main clauses.

(a) Enzymes are used in industry.

(b) Cheetahs are the fastest land animals.

(c) The contestant performed the song.

(d) Gardening is seasonal work.

(e) We are revising hard.

(f) One of the reactive metals is zinc.

Other clauses

2   Add a main clause to each subordinate clause to complete each of these sentences.

(a) In order to obtain a meal, ...

(b) Even though we were exhausted, ...

(c) As I reached the top of the mountain, ...

(d) Because the platform was so crowded, ...

> A **subordinate clause** does not express a complete idea; you need more information (the main clause).

3   Underline the relative clauses in these sentences.

(a) Waste water from metal ore mines, which is often highly acidic, contains small amounts of toxic metals.

(b) Israel, whose army grew during the war, was under attack from five enemies.

(c) Some minerals, which cannot be seen, are dissolved in the water and carried along in the flow.

(d) Jane's Aunt Reed, who does not care for Jane, sends her away to boarding school.

(e) River embankments are created by the deposition process, which takes place during flooding.

> A **relative clause** is a type of subordinate clause that begins with a relative pronoun.

Simple sentences

A **simple sentence** consists of a single main clause with a finite verb. It can be used effectively in writing to present a viewpoint or in imaginative writing.

A subject and one verb

1   Underline and label the **subject** (S), **verb** (V) and **object** (O) in each of these sentences.

(a)   The materials form natural embankments.

(b)   The bypass plans threaten local biodiversity.

(c)   Human activity is damaging the river habitats.

2   Rewrite these simple sentences as questions by changing the word order.

(a)   Ellipses can create tension in a piece of fiction.

....

(b)   This type of river bend is called a meander.

....

Using simple sentences

3   (a)   Draw lines to match each simple sentence with the correct longer sentence. [Simple sentence] shows the position of the simple sentence.

Simple sentence	Longer sentence
Sea water can kill land plants.	Outside, rain battered the windows, through which he could just make out the autumn leaves as they danced around the garden and settled on the surface of the pond. [simple sentence]
This is active transport.	Cells may need to transport molecules against a concentration gradient or transport molecules that are too big to diffuse through the cell membrane. [simple sentence]
Gardening was out of the question.	[simple sentence] When the concentration of mineral salts in the soil is higher than that inside the roots, the roots cannot take up water by osmosis.

(b)   Increase the impact of the passages below by adding a simple sentence where indicated.

(i)   Charity fun runs are open to all and provide you with good exercise, good friendships and

good fun. ....

(ii)   ....
When we were finally called together, they lined us up and got us into our harnesses; gave us a terrifyingly brief explanation of what to do and had us walking over to the climbing wall.

Compound sentences

A **compound sentence** contains two or more main clauses linked by a coordinating conjunction.

Linked main clauses

1 Rewrite each pair of sentences as a compound sentence using an appropriate coordinating conjunction from this box. You won't need all the conjunctions.

and	but	for	or	so	yet

(a) I like history. Sam likes geography.

....

(b) The teacher explained the theory. She made it seem easy.

....

(c) Water can be obtained from natural lakes. It can be obtained from reservoirs.

....

(d) Water can become contaminated. It needs to be treated before consumption.

....

(e) Building on floodplains increases the risk of flooding. It is still a common practice.

....

Using compound sentences

2 Rewrite this paragraph to improve the flow. Use conjunctions from the box in Question 1 to change some of the simple sentences into compound sentences.

Gina noticed that the man ahead of her had stopped. She stepped to one side to avoid hitting him as she passed by. She passed him. He turned towards her. His face was contorted. Was he smiling? Was he angry? The man's eyes had laughter lines around the edges. Gina felt uncomfortable under his gaze. She tried to look away.

....

....

....

....

....

....

Complex sentences

In a **complex sentence**, one clause is dependent on another clause for meaning.

Subordinate clauses

> **Guided**

1 Change these simple sentences into complex sentences by adding a subordinate clause after each bold subordinating conjunction.

    (a) **After** <u>we had stopped for pizza on our way home,</u> we didn't eat our dinner.

    (b) The only thing that matters, **although** ...., is winning.

    (c) We decided not to go to the beach **once** ....

    (d) **Unless** ...., we didn't wear our coats.

> A subordinate clause can come at the beginning, in the middle or at the end of a complex sentence.

Relative clauses

2 Add an appropriate relative pronoun to each of these sentences.

    (a) Mitosis is the process .... causes cells to divide.

    (b) The growth of human babies, ... is regularly checked by measuring them, includes mass and length.

    (c) Macbeth, ... was persuaded to kill Duncan, was tortured by insecurity and guilt.

    (d) Lady Macbeth, ... ambitions motivated her actions, descended into madness.

> A relative clause can only go in the middle or at the end of a complex sentence.

Using complex sentences

3 Rewrite each pair of sentences as a single complex sentence, using an appropriate subordinating conjunction or relative pronoun.

    (a)
> The blunt end of a drumlin faces the direction of ice flow. The tapered end points in the direction of glacial flow.

    ....

    ....

    (b)
> My aunt had come to stay. She was a stern, grey-faced woman.

    ....

    ....

Using quotations

You can use **quotations** from a text to provide evidence for your idea or argument.

Short quotations

1   Decide which part of each sentence is likely to be a short quotation. Add quotation marks where you think they should be placed.

(a)   The *Guinness Book of World Records* has two entries for what it calls the world's largest living tree.

(b)   The environmentalists called for a halt to unsustainable tourism, citing unacceptable levels of noise pollution, litter and erosion as the main reasons.

(c)   Daphne Du Maurier increases the sense of desolation and loneliness by pointing out that the little lattice windows gaped forlorn.

(d)   In *Remember*, Christina Rossetti speaks directly to the reader, repeatedly urging them to remember me.

(e)   It is ironic that, in Act 1, Scene 2, Duncan calls Macbeth valiant cousin! and worthy gentleman! because Macbeth will betray his respect and trust later in the play.

Longer quotations

2   Decide which part of each extract is likely to be a long quotation. Add a colon and quotation marks where you think they should be placed.

(a)   Macbeth suggests that the witches are part of the supernatural world when he states in his letter to Lady Macbeth in Act 1, Scene 5 I have learned by the perfectest report, they have more in them than mortal knowledge.

(b)   The persona's bitter jealousy is only made clear towards the end of the poem … Oh sir, she smiled, no doubt, / Whene'er I passed her; but who passed without / Much the same smile?

(c)   Jane's outburst finally frees her from the oppressive Reeds I am glad you are no relation of mine. I will never call you aunt again as long as I live.

> You can use a colon to introduce a longer quotation.

Synonyms

Synonyms are words with the same or a very similar meaning.

Key words

1   Write three synonyms for each of these words.

(a)   suggest   ....

(b)   a lot   ....

(c)   example   ....

(d)   similarly   ....

Repetition and imprecise language

2   (a)   Circle the imprecise language in each sentence.

(i)   He gets lots of money from his job.

(ii)   The king got lots of bad comments about how he did his job.

(iii)   The writer talks about love and stuff in the poems.

(b)   Write a more precise version of each sentence using the words and phrases below.

criticism	explores	leadership
nature of relationships	received	salary	earns

(i)   ....

(ii)   ....

(iii)   ....

3   Replace the repeated words in this passage with more precise synonyms.

Fashion is something to talk about and like with your friends. If all your friends like
fashion and like to wear the same fashions, then you can swap clothes and tell them if
you like how they look.

Checking your work

Correcting a few SPaG mistakes at the end of the exam might make the difference you need to improve your grade.

1   Look at a student's response to this science question. Check it carefully for the following:

  • common spelling errors – e.g. misspelled root words when a suffix has been added

  • punctuation errors – e.g. misplaced apostrophes

  • grammatical errors – e.g. missing or repeated words

  • organisational errors – e.g. missed paragraph breaks.

Cross out and correct all the errors you can find. Write your corrections above the errors. Add any missing words using the ^ symbol. Add any paragraph breaks using the **//** symbol.

> Young children are immunised against a range of infectious diseases.
> Explain how immunisation protects them from these diseases.
>
> Immunisation means making somone immune to a disese by giving them a vacine. The vacine contains an inactive from of the pathogen that causes the disese. As these are not active pathogens, the vacine will not make the person suffer from the disese. The vacine contains pathogen antigens. Puting these antigens into a childs body causes an imune response which means that lymphocytes that match these particuler antigens become activated and produce many matching lymphocyte's and antibodie's. some of the lymphocytes become memry lymphocytes and remain in the blood for along time. If the live pathogen gets the body at a latter time, the memry lymphocytes are already there to reconise the antigens on the pathogen and cause an imune response. This response is large rapid because huge numbers of antibodies is produced very quickley. The antibodys attack and kill the pathogens before they can make the child ill.

Correcting errors

When you check your work, you may wish to correct something. You can do this by **deleting**, **correcting** or **adding** words.

1   Read the opening section of a student's response to this speech-writing task. Find and correct these errors in the text:

- three duplicate words. Draw a single line through any words to delete.

- two vague or informal terms to correct. Draw a line through the word or phrase and write the correction above it.

- three missing words to add. Use ∧ to insert a word. Write the missing word on the line above.

- two missing new paragraphs. Use the **//** symbol to show where the new paragraph should start.

- seven incorrect words, homophones or near homophones.

- two spelling errors. Draw a line through the word or phrase and write the correction above it.

Write a speech to be given in front of your local council, explaining your viewpoint on the following statement.

Public transport where I live could and should be better.

Public transport is at the heart of a thryving economy. It lets people to travel travel to work, to visit cultural attractions and to be aparte of local community. Unfortunately, for those of us who live in remote parts of the country, it can be very difficult too integrate with the community because there is a disappointing lack of access to the nearest town. From my place, there only one bus each hour to Cottenham and it does not run after 6 o'clock. This means that people in my village are not able to intend any evening events or get connecting transport from any other citys, limiting their cultural experiences and employment opportunitys. I propose that an hourly service until midnight to to and from Cottenham to its satellite villages should be introduced. My estimate shows suggests that the cost of runnin the bigger service would be less then the of the annual spring fare and would increase spending in Cottenham centre significantly.

Improving answers: History

This extract from a student's answer to a History question contains a number of errors, as well as missed opportunities to score highly for SPaG.

1   Read the response carefully. Cross out and correct the following errors:

 • nine spelling errors

 • nine punctuation errors

 • four capital letter errors

 • one missing paragraph break (use the **//** symbol)

 • two inappropriate contractions

 • one misused conjunction.

Write any corrections on the line above the error.

> Mao launched the 'Anti-Rightist' purge because he wanted to end widespread critisism of the Chinese Communist Party CCP. During the hundred flowers campain, Mao allowed people to criticise his government. This led economists to critiscise the first five-year Plan and scientists and experts to criticise the way the ccp ran factories Student's went further and criticised Maos rule of china. They demanded freedom and democrecy, which Mao didn't want to allow. Nevertheless, Mao introduced the Anti Rightist purge to humilliate and inprison dangerous criticks of his government. Their is also evidence that Mao had planned to launch the 'Anti-Rightist' purge. From 1949 Mao was worried that bureucrats were taking over the CCP and that there were still enemies of communism who hadn't been weeded out Therefore; he launched the 'Anti-Rightist' purge to get rid of bureaucrats and the enimies of the CCP (people who had criticised the government during the Hundred Flowers campaign.

2   Rewrite one sentence from the response that you would like to improve.

....

....

Improving answers: Geography

This extract from a student's answer to a Geography question contains a number of errors, as well as missed opportunities to score highly for SPaG.

1   Read the response carefully. Cross out and correct the following errors:

- six spelling errors

- seven punctuation errors

- six capital letter errors

- one missing paragraph break (use the **//** symbol)

- one misused conjunction.

Write any corrections on the line above the error.

> Germany, a developed country, is inversting in finding technologes to increase the efficiency of wind turbines. After the 2011 japanese nuclear accidents, Germanys government developed a new plan for increasing renewable energy production, this had a clear focus on offshore wind farms. A second reason for developing sustainable energy resources is that germany plans to reduce greenhouse gas emissons by 40 per cent by 2022 to help reduce the impact of Global Warming. China a developing country contributes 29 per cent to global carbon emissions — more than any other country. China also has seven of the world's ten most poluted cities and it burns more coal than the usa, Europe and Japan combined. For example, Chinas renewable energy law, 2006, aims to develop renewable energy resources. China is now a leading sollar power producer. The solar plant being built in the gobi desert could produce enegy for one million homes in the future. China's awareness of it's energy needs has increased takeup of solar panels across the country

2   Rewrite one sentence from the response that you would like to improve.

....

....

Improving answers: Religious Studies

This extract from a student's answer to a Religious Studies question contains a number of errors, as well as missed opportunities to score highly for SPaG.

1   Read the response carefully. Cross out and correct the following errors:

- eleven spelling errors
- seven punctuation errors
- two informal phrases that need rewriting
- two missing paragraph breaks (use the **//** symbol).

Write any corrections on the line above the error.

Christans have diffrent ideas and beliefs about why people suffer and often they question what's the point of suffering. Many Christians would agree that it is human beings who do evile things, and cause a large amount of suffring in the world. Conversely, every day we see terorist attacks on the television and we also hear of murders and other serious crimes. However this cannot explain other happenings that could also be seen as evil, such as natural disasters. Some Christians beleive that in some circomstances, suffering can lead to personel growth. These are circumstances when the saying what doesn't kill you makes you stronger comes into play. Christians also understand that suffering can sometimes bring out the worst in people and can seem a waste of time. In some cases, it can lead to a crisis.

of faith for some Christians, when they begin to doubt their beliefs in the existence of God. In the end Christians accept that there are limits to what human beings can fuly understand or explain about evil and suffering they are comforted in the belief that, because of the suffering experenced by Jesus during the crucfixion and during his time on Earth, God can at least understand and relate to human misery and pain

2   Rewrite one sentence from the response that you would like to improve.

....

....

Improving answers: Biology

This student's answer to a Biology question contains a number of errors, as well as missed opportunities for making the writing clearer.

1   Read the response carefully. Cross out and correct the following errors:

- thirteen spelling errors

- six punctuation errors

- two capital letter errors

- one missing paragraph break (use the // symbol)

- three examples of the wrong word being used (one of which would lose marks for Biology subject knowledge)

- two examples of incorrect subject–verb agreement.

Write any corrections on the line above the error.

> mitosis is the cell-division process which produces two Diploid daughter cells from one parent cell. During mitisis, each daughter cell recieves a copy of evry chromosome in the parent cell, which means that they are genitically identical mitosis is used in asexual reproduction and produces ofspring that are genetically identical to the one parent In mieosis, four daugter cells are produced from one parant cell. Each daughter cell are haploid and have copys of only half the chromosomes of the diploid parent cell. This produces gametes, that are genetically diffrent to each other. Meiosis occurs before asexual reproduction in which two gametes fuse to form a fertilised egg cell that is diploid. The varition in the gametes means that the offspring difer genetically form each other and from the two parents

2   Rewrite one sentence from the response that you would like to improve.

....

....

> Although there are no SPaG marks allocated specifically for Biology, clear, correct writing will help you effectively express your reasoning in extended answers.

Improving answers: Chemistry

This student's answer to a Chemistry question contains a number of errors, as well as missed opportunities for making the writing clearer.

1   Read the response carefully. Cross out and correct the following errors:

- eight spelling errors

- four punctuation errors

- three capital letter errors

- one missing paragraph break (use the **//** symbol)

- four examples of the wrong word being used

- two inappropriate abbreviations

- one missing conjunction

- two comparative errors.

Write any corrections on the line above the error.

> Although there are no SPaG marks allocated specifically for Chemistry, clear, correct writing will help you effectively express your reasoning in extended answers.

i think the data show that the reaction in experment 2 is 9x faster than the same reation in experiment 1. There are two reasons for the greatest rate of reaction in experiment 2. Firstly the particals in the powder have a greater surface area than the particles in the stuff used in experiment 1. This means that most particles are exposed to the acid & their are more frequant collisions between reactent particles so the rate of reaction is greater. The increased rate of reaction is also due to the increased temprature of the acid. The reactant particles in Experiment 2 have more energy then those in experiment 1. therefore, a greater proportion of them have the activation energy or more this means that the frequency of successful colisions is greater, causing a greater rate of reaction. It would of been better to vary the size of the particles and the temperature seperately, but the data clearly show that the rate of reaction in experiment 1 is greater than in experiment 2

2   Rewrite one sentence from the response that you would like to improve.

....

....

Improving answers: Physics

This student's answer to a Physics question contains a number of errors, as well as missed opportunities for making the writing clearer.

1   Read the response carefully. Cross out and correct the following errors:

- eight spelling errors

- six punctuation errors

- four capital letter errors

- four examples of the wrong word being used

- one inappropriate abbreviation

- one inappropriate contraction

- one subject–verb agreement error

- two comparative errors.

Write any corrections on the line above the error.

> Power is the rate of doing werk & is measured in Watts. When people climb
> a hill, they are doing work against gravaty, and the energy transfered is
> the force (their wieght) multiplied by the distrance moved in the direction
> of the force up the hill. If the two people has the same weight as they
> have both climbed the same distance in theory they've both transferred
> the same amount of enargy. alan exerted the greatest power because
> he gained the height in a shortest time. However this answer may not be
> correct if there weights are not the same. it also asumes that the human
> body is totally eficent which its not. As bev was walking for longer: she will
> waist more energy and so will of transferred more energy altogether

2   Rewrite one sentence from the response that you would like to improve.

....

....

> Although there are no SPaG marks allocated specifically
> for Physics, clear, correct writing will help you effectively
> express your reasoning in extended answers.

Improving answers: English Literature

This extract from a student's answer to an English Literature question contains a number of errors, as well as missed opportunities to score highly for SPaG.

1   Read the response carefully. Cross out and correct the following errors:

- ten spelling errors

- twelve punctuation errors

- four capital letter errors

- three examples of wrong words being used

- two missed paragraph breaks (use the // symbol)

- two examples of the wrong tense for English Literature responses.

Write any corrections on the line above the error.

Charles Dicken's A Christmas Carol is set in victorian London and depicts a range of issues that dickens personally experienced growing up. It convays a message that was dear to Dickens' heart, namely that of social responsability. Dickens felt very strongly that the inequality in Victorian England was a grave injustice and sort to influnce his reader's to change there attitudes and behaviour towards these less fortunate than themselves In the opening Stave Dickens depicted Scrooge as a deeply unpleasant character almost supernaturally so, and this sets up the atmasphere for the rest of the novel. scrooge is a "tight-fisted hand" and a squeezing, wrenching, grasping, scraping … old sinner. This list of unpleasant adjectives immediatley creates an impression of Scrooge as an agressive and intimidating charachter. Dickens uses the extended comparason of the weather to help the reader recognise just how cold hearted Scrooge was. "No wind that blew was bitterer than he" … no pelting rain less open to entreaty." The adjective bitterer gives a strong sense that nothing is more unpleasant to experience than the prescence of Mr Scrooge

2   Rewrite one sentence from the response that you would like to improve.

....

....

Improving answers: English Language

This extract from a student's answer to an English Language imaginative writing question contains a number of errors, as well as missed opportunities to score highly for SPaG.

1 Read the response carefully. Cross out and correct the following errors:

- seven spelling errors

- four punctuation errors

- four examples of the wrong word being used

- one example of two words which should be one word

- one phrase that needs rewriting

- three examples of incorrect tense for English Language responses.

Write any corrections on the line above the error.

Sunlight dapples on dense foliage and the deep grass below. The sounds of the waves on the coast where calm, sweeping across the beach as they ozed in and out off the shore. Swaying in the gentle breese, palms cast shadows across the white hot sand. Scattered across the beach, shells beckon to the lagoon. This was a sight of tranquillity, a site of calm. Drifting in the breeze, birdsong flavoured the air.

The silence was shatterred by the roar from the scarlet creature devouring every inch of the once beautiful island that got in it's path. The creeping snake like vines twisted and slivered around the burning trunks as if brought to life by the fire. Black, now an ommniprescent shade in the sky, transforms by the plumes of smoke being coffed out from the fire, aggressively loomed above. Birds scatterred from the molten blaze as it destroyed their homes, their helpless cry's eerie and haunting as they fled the island into the blackened sky. Smoke filled the air as the fire raged on.

2 Rewrite one sentence from the response that you would like to improve.

....

....

Answers

ENGLISH FOR EXAMS

1. Standard English

1 Suggested answers:

Spoken English (non-Standard)	Written English (Standard)
Me and Danny are going down town.	Danny and I are going into the town centre.
I don't want nuthin'.	I don't want anything.
That was pretty sick.	That was very good.
Get in!	Well done! / That's great!
What d'ya want?	What do you want? / What would you like?

2 Suggested answer:

Russian historians
~~Some Russian blokes~~ such as Zubok and Pleshakov have been
investigating secret files
~~poking their nose into secret files stashed away~~ in the Soviet
reveal how Russian leaders
Union. These files ~~go on about how bigwigs in Russia~~ during the
evade conflict
Cold War were trying to ~~wheedle out of argy-bargy~~ with the USA.

shows America's part in the Cold War at this time.
This ~~just goes to show that America was the bad-guy~~.

3 Suggested answers:

(a) Hello. How are you?

(b) That examination was very straightforward.

(c) It is estimated that approximately one third of the world's population identifies as Christian.

2. Formal and informal language

1 (a) Informal   (b) Formal

   (c) Formal   (d) Informal

2 (a) ii   (b) i   (c) iv   (d) iii

3 Suggested answers:

(a) to apologise

(b) to establish, to start, to organise

(c) to consider, to ponder, to reflect

4 Suggested answer: The novelist uses contemporary slang to reflect the language used by young people.

SPELLING

3. Double letters

1 (a) padding   (b) jabbing

   (c) shopping   (d) begging

2 (a) flattening   (b) answered   (c) omitted

   (d) regretted   (e) happening   (f) referring

3 (a) He **entered** the house.

(b) We'll be **opening** the new department next week.

(c) She **rebelled** against the establishment.

(d) Tell me what is **upsetting** you.

(e) **Straightening** his back, he moved from the chair.

4. Silent letters

1 (a) sword   (b) wom**b**   (c) nestle

   (d) mortgage   (e) **k**napsack   (f) ascend

   (g) would   (h) **c**haos   (i) aisle

   (j) wriggle

2 (b) generally (unstressed e)   (c) family (unstressed i)

   (d) definitely (unstressed i)   (e) colonel (unstressed o)

   (f) business (unstressed i)   (g) colleague (unstressed u)

   (h) interesting (unstressed e)   (i) company (unstressed a)

3 (a) women   (b) secret   (c) calendar

   (d) wordsearch   (e) wor**k**   (f) dollar

5. Plurals: adding -s and -es

1 (a) churches   (b) novels   (c) images   (d) wishes

   (e) cells   (f) suffixes   (g) historians

   (h) chemicals

2 The following bold words should be circled:

(a) **Viruses** can infect all living things.

(b) At this time, people refused to pay their **taxes**.

(c) The **towns** were built on river estuaries.

(d) The library contained many rare and valuable **books**.

(e) Liam washed the **dishes** under protest.

(f) The extraction **processes** are quite complicated.

3 (a) The ~~studentes~~ used compasses ✓ to find
students
   the correct route, as well as ~~mapes~~ and GPS ~~devicees~~.
maps   devices

(b) The poems ✓ and ~~snatchs~~ of ~~songes~~ in the anthology cover a
snatches songs
   range of ~~subjectes~~.
subjects

(c) ~~Prefixs~~ are added at the beginnings ✓ of words ✓ to change
Prefixes
   ~~meaninges~~.
meanings

6. Plurals: words ending -y

1 (a) abbeys   (b) journeys   (c) kidneys

   (d) storeys   (e) essays   (f) valleys

2 (a) colonies   (b) technologies

   (c) armies   (d) histories

   (e) studies   (f) enemies

3 (a) babies   (b) screenplays   (c) cities

   (d) libraries   (e) centuries   (f) holidays

   (g) supplies   (h) causeways

4 Answers will vary, but will include three of the following words:

allergies   alleys   armies   delays   railways

quays   stories   gullies   victories

7. Plurals: other endings

1 The following words should be circled:

volcano (volcanoes)   hero (heroes)

embargo (embargoes)   tomato (tomatoes)

mosquito (mosquitoes)

2 Suggested answers:

tornado(e)s   mango(e)s   ghetto(e)s
zero(e)s   flamingo(e)s

3 (a) The **chefs** used **knives**.

(b) The **wharves** contained **loaves** for distribution.

(c) The **thieves** have raided all the **safes** in the bank.

4 (a) chiefs   (b) shelves   (c) gulfs

   (d) leaves   (e) calves   (f) beliefs

8. Irregular plurals

1 (a) fish   (c) aircraft   (d) Sioux

   (f) headquarters   (g) offspring   (h) haddock

   (i) species   (l) series

2 Fish is the odd one out because the plural can be either fish or fishes.

3 (a) axes   (b) criteria   (c) millennia

   (d) diseases   (e) analyses   (f) nuclei

   (g) formulas/formulae   (h) heroes   (i) halves

   (j) deltas   (k) lice   (l) teeth

4 (a) children   (b) women   (c) bacteria

   (d) mice   (e) crises   (f) fungi (or funguses)

9. Prefixes

1 (a) **dis**advantage   (b) **a**typical   (c) **il**literate

   (d) **un**affordable   (e) **un**believable   (f) **anti**hero

   (g) **ir**rational   (h) **de**clutter

2 Suggested answers:

Word	Prefix meaning	Another word with that prefix
extraordinary	outside of / beyond / more than	extraterrestrial
overcook	too much	overarching
upgrade	make or move higher	uphill
autobiography	self	automobile
outdo	go beyond	outrun

3 (a) The adults were considered to be **un**ruly and **dis**courteous.

   (b) The museum had many **inter**active exhibits.

   (c) The phone contract included only two **mega**bytes of data.

   (d) **Co**operation between water companies has resulted in enough water to meet demands, despite **un**even rainfall.

   (e) Symptoms of stress include **hyper**sensitivity to stimuli and **ir**regular sleep patterns.

10. Suffixes: changes to word endings

1 (a)

thoughtless	nameless
useless	merciless

   (b)

acidify	beautify
dignify	codify

   (c)

alluring	handwriting
dying	hurrying

2 (a), (b) and (c)

Possible answers:

- less – root word ends with a vowel: add 'less'
- less – root word ends with a 'y': change 'y' to 'i'
- ify – root word ends in an 'e': drop the 'e' and add 'ify'
- ing – root word ends with a consonant and a 'y': keep the 'y'
- ing – root word ends in 'ie': change the 'ie' to a 'y'.

3 (a) families   (b) disposable   (c) shapeless   (d) amplify

11. Suffixes: adding to root words

1 (b) introduc**ing**, introduc**ed**, introduc**tion**

   (c) decid**ing**, decid**ed**, deci**sion**

   (d) discuss**ing**, discuss**ion**, discuss**ed**

   (e) politic**al**, politic**ian**

   (f) music**al**, music**ian**

2 (a) ambition   (b) solution   (c) antisocial

   (d) essential   (e) available   (f) visible

   (g) experience   (h) importance

3 (a) potential   (b) official

   (c) suspicion   (d) optician

4 (a) redund**ant**   (b) oppon**ent**

   (c) nutri**tion**   (d) inci**sion**

12. Homophones: contractions

1

it's	This is a contraction that means **it is**. The apostrophe shows where the letter 'i' has been removed.
its	This is a possessive pronoun that means **belonging to it**. It never has an apostrophe.
they're	This is a contraction that means **they are**. The apostrophe shows where the letter 'a' has been removed.
their	This is a possessive pronoun that means **belonging to them**.
there	This shows the **place or position of something**.
your	This is a possessive pronoun that means **belonging to you**.
you're	This is a contraction that means **you are**. The apostrophe shows where the letter 'a' has been removed.

2 The following bold words should be circled:

   (a) **It's** time for the storm to do **its** worst.

   (b) "Are you sure **your** teacher said that **your** homework was good?"

   (c) "**There** is no time to waste. **They're** catching us up. Look – over **there**!"

   (d) "**You're** going to be in trouble. You shouldn't have eaten **their** sandwiches!"

3 Suggested answers:

They're going to be so happy to be invited to **your** birthday party.

You're not going to believe who I saw **there**.

It's past **their** bedtime.

13. Homophones: common groups

1 Suggested answers:

   (a) **To**: I went **to** the park. (*meaning – direction*)

   (b) **Too**: I went to the park and my friend came **too**. (*meaning – as well or also*)

   (c) **Two**: There are **two** parks. (*meaning – number*)

2

here	This is an adverb that means **in this place**. It indicates position.
hear	This is a verb that means **listen**.
past	This is an adverb that means **by** (indicating direction), or **gone by** (indicating time).
passed	This is a verb in the past tense that means **approved** or **succeeded**.
allowed	This is a verb in the past tense that means **permitted**.
aloud	This is an adverb that means **audibly**.

3   The following bold words should be circled:

(a)   What **ails** thee, knight at arms?

(b)   She was fine until she **ate** too many cakes.

(c)   The **altar** was positioned in the centre of the church.

(d)   The band was **banned** from the tour.

(e)   Homework is **due** on Monday

(f)   It was a **lapse** in judgement.

(g)   In this **scene** Shakespeare introduces Lady Macbeth.

14. Common spelling errors

1   The following bold words should be circled:

(a)   We are going to work at **our** house.

(b)   We should **devise** a revision method that works for us.

(c)   My teacher's **advice** was to create a timetable.

(d)   My sister could not **accept** that I was a better singer than her.

(e)   The Romantic poets **preceded** the Liverpool Poets.

(f)   She stormed **off** in a rage.

(g)   He was **quite quiet** and shy.

(h)   I don't often **lose** anything, **except** for my keys.

2   Suggested answers:

(a)   Though – your sentence will show the meaning 'despite the fact that.' e.g. *Even **though** it was raining, we didn't wear our boots.*

(b)   Through – your sentence will show that this is a preposition e.g. *She walked **through** the door.*

(c)   Thought – your sentence will show that this is the past tense of to think e.g. *I **thought** I understood.*

(d)   Thorough – your sentence will show the meaning 'in depth' e.g. *She gave the house a **thorough** cleaning.*

15. 'i' before 'e'

1   (a) f**ie**ld   (b) rec**ei**pt   (c) br**ie**f

(d) rec**ei**ve   (e) sh**ie**ld   (f) misch**ie**f

(g) dec**ei**ve   (h) perc**ei**ve

2   Suggested answers:

(a)   We all need **protein** in our diet for building and repairing cells.

(b)   The government used conflict as an excuse to **seize** land from Indian tribes.

(c)   **Caffeine** can be found in coffee, tea and some fizzy drinks.

3   (a) (i) anc**ie**nt   (ii) sc**ie**nce   (iii) effic**ie**nt

(b)   These words are unusual because 'ie' is used after a 'c' as it doesn't make the 'ee' sound.

16. Spellings for GCSE History

1

government	consequence	interpretation	propaganda
persecution	Roosevelt	inhibited	contemporary
parliament	Bolshevik	abolitionists	Versailles
Mao Tse-tung	suffrage		

2   Answers will vary.

3   Suggested answers:

- interpretation – English Literature, Religious Studies, Sciences
- propaganda – English Language, Religious Studies
- persecution – Religious Studies

17. Spellings for GCSE Geography

1

environment	hydraulic	cyclone	malnourishment
tectonic	reservoir	decentralisation	tsunami
biome	igneous	gentrification	precipitation
interdependence	congestion		

2   Answers will vary.

3   Answers will vary.

18. Spellings for GCSE Religious Studies

1

atheist	benevolent	omniscient	monotheistic
Eucharist	contemporary	synagogue	euthanasia
resurrected	dharma	transcendence	Qur'an
mitzvah	samsara	Shi'a	

2   Answers will vary.

3   Answers will vary.

19. Spellings for GCSE Biology

1

photosynthesis	endoscope	chlorophyll	independent
accommodation	electrolysis	electrolyte	haemoglobin
breathe (verb)	breath (noun)	alleles	deficiency
homozygous	heterozygous	coronary	diaphragm
anaerobic	plaque		

2   Answers will vary.

3   Suggested answers:

- accommodation – Geography, English Language
- electrolysis/electrolyte – Chemistry
- breathe/breath – English Language, English Literature
- deficiency – History, Geography, English Language

20. Spellings for GCSE Chemistry

1

aqueous	decolourised	chromatography	covalent
buckminsterfullerene	crystallography	Avogadro	magnesium
reversible	catalyst	meiosis	equilibrium
Le Chatelier's	viscosity	homologous	

2   Answers will vary.

3   Answers will vary.

21. Spellings for GCSE Physics

1

seismic	velocity	oscilloscope	longitudinal
nuclear fission	neutron	coulomb	infrared
emission	efficiency	anomaly	translucent
inertia	satellite	dissipated	

2   Answers will vary.

3   Answers will vary.

22. Spellings for GCSE English Literature

1

soliloquy	rhyme	stanza	pathetic fallacy
allegorical	rhythm	anthropomorphism	dialogue
Iambic pentameter	metaphor	euphemism	onomatopoeia

2   Answers will vary.

3   Answers will vary.

23. Spellings for English Language

1

simile	colloquialism	rhetorical	hyperbole
inference	synonym	sibilance	apostrophe
ellipses	technique	cliché	synthesis
biased	evidence	convey	

2 Answers will vary.

3 Suggested answers:
  - inference – English Literature, History
  - synthesis – Biology, Chemistry
  - biased – History
  - evidence – Sciences, History, English Literature
  - convey – History, English Literature, Art

PUNCTUATION

24. Capital letters

1 (a) **Y**ou are fettered," said Scrooge, trembling. "**T**ell me why?"

  (b) "**B**ah," said Scrooge. "**H**umbug."

  (c) "**C**hristmas a humbug, uncle!" said Scrooge's nephew. "**Y**ou don't mean that, I am sure."

2 The following words should be corrected:

  (a) **S**ir **A**rthur **C**onan **D**oyle   (b) **E**xeter

  (e) **H**indu   (h) **E**aster

3 (a) '**A** **M**idsummer **N**ight's **D**ream', written by **W**illiam **S**hakespeare, is a complex tale of magic and mayhem.

  (b) **T**he electromagnetic spectrum is a continuous range of wavelengths.

  (c) **I**t is estimated that **J**ulius **C**aesar was born in **R**ome in **J**uly 100 **BC**.

  (d) **I** think religion can be defined as a set of beliefs concerning the cause, purpose and nature of the universe.

25. Sentence endings

1 Check that you have used a full stop at the end of your sentences and that each sentence fulfils the brief given.
  Suggested answers:

Type of sentence	Your example
(a) a sentence that gives a fact	Queen Elizabeth II's coronation took place on 2nd June 1953.
(b) a sentence that gives an opinion	Women make better politicians than men.
(c) a sentence that gives a command	Wear eye protection and wash your hands after the experiment.

2 Suggested answers:

Type of question	Your example
(a) question word	**Which** ingredient shall I add first?
(b) question tag	He really likes that programme, **doesn't he**?
(c) inversion	**Is it** usual to eat cheese and jam together?

3 (a) The shout of "Gas!" in Wilfred Owen's poem takes us to the heart of the battlefield.

  (b) "I can't believe the amount of repeats on TV these days!" said Josie.

  (c) We must not be afraid of our exams. We must fight for our results!

26. Commas for extra information

1 (a) Macbeth, the murderer of Duncan, seized the crown by foul means.

  (b) Dawlish Warren, near Exeter and Dawlish, is a Blue Flag family resort.

2 (a) Lady Macbeth, **whose** persuasion led her husband to kill Duncan, fell into madness at the end of the play.

  (b) I thanked my tutor, **who** had helped me to work on a revision timetable.

  (c) Fruit, **which** should form part of a daily diet, is a source of essential nutrients.

27. Commas in lists

1 (a) I will either bake chocolate cake, apple pie or banana cake tonight.

  (b) Super fruits are thought to contain antioxidants, fibre, vitamins and minerals.

2 (a) This evening, I could go swimming, play basketball or go to the gym.

  (b) At the start of the novel, Scrooge could be described as miserly, greedy and full of hate.

3 (a) Lady Macbeth's disturbed, frenzied mood continues throughout this scene.

  (b) This is an insightful, well-observed essay.

4 (a) This is an instruction not to call someone else 'stupid'.

  (b) Someone is being called stupid for thinking of calling (telephoning) the person referred to as 'him'.

28. Avoiding comma splicing

1 (a) Tropical rainforests and mountainous areas receive more water than they lose. This results in a water surplus.

  (b) Tropical rainforests and mountainous areas receive more water than they lose so this results in a water surplus.

2 One of these three ways:
  - Use a full stop to make **two separate sentences**, e.g. *The narrative is third person. **The** author has used the pronouns 'he' and 'she'.*
  - When appropriate, you can use a comma followed by a **conjunction**, e.g. *The narrative is third person, so the author has used the pronouns 'he' and 'she'.*
  - Where the two independent clauses are linked in meaning, you can use a **semi-colon** to separate the clauses, e.g. *The narrative is third person; the author has used the pronouns 'he' and 'she'.*

3 Suggested answers:

  (a) We still live in a society where men dominate political spheres, but women also have the power to change the policies that constrain us.

  (b) Offenders who leave after a longer time get more help readjusting to normal life; those on shorter sentences don't.

  (c) I don't really care for science. On the other hand, I'd rather study science than maths.

29. Avoiding other comma errors

1 (a) The girl <u>who copied my work</u> is in the canteen.

  (b) The car <u>with the chipped paintwork</u> damaged my bicycle.

  (c) One of the reasons why people in developing countries use water <u>that is polluted with animal and human waste</u> is because they have no other choice due to lack of piped water.

2 (i) a   (ii) b

3 In sentence (a), there is only one photograph and the fact that it shows a piece of slate is additional, non-vital information. In sentence (b), the clause 'that shows a piece of slate' is differentiating this photo from one or more others that show different types of rock.

30. Colons

1 (a) For my revision I need the following: some sticky notes, some highlighter pens and some A4 paper.

(b) Macbeth could be described in many ways: easily persuaded, overly ambitious and murderous.

(c) I have two options here: continue revising or watch football.

2 Possible answers:

For my revision I need the following:

- some sticky notes
- some highlighter pens
- some A4 paper.

Macbeth could be described in many ways:

- easily persuaded
- overly ambitious
- murderous.

I have two options here:

- continue revising
- watch football.

3 (a) These worms are a type of zombie worm: they have no eyes or mouth.

(b) Hooke's microscope was not very powerful: the glass lenses were of poor quality.

31. Semi-colons

1 In Jane Austen's 'Pride and Prejudice', the Bennet sisters are: Jane, who is beautiful and thoughtful; Elizabeth, who is the lively and witty main character of the novel; Mary, who is the serious and plain member of the family; Catherine or 'Kitty', who is easily led by her younger sister; and Lydia, who is frivolous, headstrong and thoughtless.

2 (a) Simon likes hot curry; William won't eat it.

(b) There was nowhere to sit in the library; it was not possible to work.

(c) I didn't do my homework; I'm now in detention.

3 (a) Example answer: The soup options are leek and potato; broccoli and stilton; and carrot and coriander.

(b) Example answer: I love my dog; she makes me laugh.

32. Brackets and dashes

1 (a) Marie Curie (who discovered radium) was a Polish and naturalised-French physicist.

(b) In the Dartmoor National Park you will find ponies, forests and tors (rock formations).

2 (a) Mr Darcy – at first hated by Elizabeth – wins her hand in marriage by the end of the novel.

(b) Respiration – the chemical reaction that releases energy from glucose – happens in mitochondria.

3 (a) In the kitchen the rule is simple – wash your hands before you start.

(b) "I just need to start my revision – hey! Is that a football match?"

4 Mitochondria – found in the cytoplasm – make most of the cell's supply of ATP (adenosine triphosphate).

33. Hyphens

1

Functions of hyphens	Example
to make some compound adjectives	self-confident
to make some compound nouns	well-being
to make some compound verbs	to sound-proof
to make compound numbers	seventy-three
to add a prefix ending with a vowel to a word starting with a vowel	semi-industrial
with other prefixes, especially before capital letters	un-American

2 (a) The government is offering a grant to small-business owners.

(b) The hyphen shows us that it is the businesses that are small. Without the hyphen, we might infer that small is describing the owners.

3 (a) My brother and my sister-in-law have a six-year-old daughter.

(b) Over-the-counter medicines are also known as non-prescription medicines.

(c) The ex-chair of the football club used up-to-date training methods.

34. Speech marks

1 (a) "I thought it was madness," he said, as he replaced the obnoxious paper in the safe, "and now I begin to fear it is disgrace."

(b) "If anyone knows, it will be Lanyon," he had thought.

(c) "I suppose, Lanyon," said he, "you and I must be the two oldest friends that Henry Jekyll has?"

2 Suggested answers:

(a) "At about 3 am on a black winter morning, I had a vague sense of discomfort," said Enfield.

(b) "It is such unscientific balderdash!" said the doctor.

(c) "Is this Mr. Hyde a person of small stature?" he inquired.

3 The reporting clause is the text outside the speech marks that tell us who is speaking. It contains a verb, such as **said** or **replied**.

35. Contractions

1 (a) (i) you're (ii) it's
(iii) we're (iv) won't
(v) would've (vi) hadn't
(vii) they'll (viii) they're

(b) (i) you are (ii) it is
(iii) we are (iv) will not
(v) would have (vi) had not
(vii) they will (viii) they are

2 Although contractions are acceptable in Standard English, you should avoid them in your exams. However, don't be afraid to use them if you're writing direct speech, as it will make the spoken words sound more natural.

3 (a) You **mustn't** use contractions in formal writing.

(b) I **shan't** miss the pressure of examinations.

(c) **What're** you doing this weekend?

(d) **He's** a talented player.

36. Possession: singular

1 (a) the girl's opinion (b) the city's approaches
(c) China's focus (d) the metaphor's power
(e) the nation's wealth

2 The following bold words should be circled:

(a) **Thomas's** bike (b) the **duchess's** retinue
(c) the **rhinoceros's** habitat (d) **Texas's** landscape

3 (a) St James's Primary School is closing after 100 years.

(b) A scatter graph's main use is to identify a relationship between two variables.

(c) The river cruise's itinerary includes visits to local heritage sites.

(d) A cactus's spines protect it from being eaten and help to reduce water loss.

(e) Putting these antigens into a child's body causes an immune response.

37. Possession: plural

1 (a) the plays' characters (b) the dogs' howls
(c) the novels' themes

2 (a) the children's toys (b) the people's rights
(c) the oxen's barn

3 (a) The geese's nests were flooded by unusually
       heavy rainfall.

   (b) Bacteria's main role in the digestive system is to help break
       down undigested food.

4 (a) and (b)

   (i)   the classes' books   (P)

   (ii)   the sheep's fleeces   (P)

   (iii) Carlos's football boots   (S)

   (iv)   Lois's ballet class   (S)

   (c)

   (v)   the teachers' suggestions   (P)

          the teacher's suggestions   (S)

   (vi)   the parents' evening   (P)

          the parent's evening   (S)

GRAMMAR

38. Articles

1 (a) a crystal   (b) a war   (c) an electrode

   (d) an hour   (e) a eulogy   (f) a university

   (g) a hospital   (h) an ambush

2 (a) 'a girl over there' could mean any girl over there. It is a vague
       statement. 'the girl over there' is referring to a specific girl.

   (b) 'an Anglo-Saxon punishment' could refer to any Anglo-Saxon
       punishment out of a number of punishments. 'the Anglo-Saxon
       punishment' refers to a specific punishment

3 (a) **A lot** of **the** prisoners suffered from poor health due to **the**
       dirty conditions.

   (b) **A** hyperbole is **an** exaggeration.

   (c) **Those** cells with one copy of each chromosome
       are haploid.

39. Different types of pronouns

1 (a) The writer uses imagery to symbolise terror. **She** also uses
       sounds that reflect her fear.

   (b) There were many reasons why Germany opposed the Treaty of
       Versailles. Firstly, **it** was seen as a Diktat.

   (c) The artists used the surrounding environment for their work.
       They did not want to merely show the landscape; instead,
       they wanted to capture the spirit of **it**.

2 Example answer:

   She had copied **my** coursework. It was not **her** work! It was **mine**!

3 The following bold words should be circled:

   (a) Elizabeth Bennet, **who** delighted in nonsense, found Mr
       Collins ridiculous.

   (b) 1907 saw the official introduction of probation officers, **whose**
       job was to check on offenders living outside prison.

   (c) The infantry, **which** was becoming more significant, embraced
       the invention of rifles.

40. Using pronouns

1 (a) Will and Jim ran back to his house because he had left his PE
       kit in his room.

       his: it is unclear whether it is Jim's house or Will's house

       he: it is unclear which one of the two boys left the PE kit behind

       his: it is unclear whose room this is referring to

       his: it is unclear whose PE kit this is referring to

   (b) Increasing frequency of storms and periods of hot, dry weather
       are both examples of weather experienced in the UK. This can
       increase the risk of flooding.
       Two types of weather are mentioned in the first sentence.
       'This' is singular and it is not clear which of the two weather
       types is being referred to. If both can increase the risk of
       flooding, the pronoun should be 'These'.

   (c) It flows naturally from side to side, around ridges in the valley
       sides called spurs.
       The pronoun 'it' starts the statement and does not refer to a
       previously mentioned noun, so there is no indication of what
       it is referring to.

2 The following bold words should be circled:

   (a) **It's** the process of repeatedly undercutting and collapsing that
       causes the formation of a steep-sided gorge.

   (b) When the river is small, **its** energy is limited.

   (c) **Its** response is large and rapid because an extensive amount of
       antibodies is produced very quickly.

3 The following bold words should be circled:

   (a) The teacher gave the homework back to **me**.

   (b) I bought a birthday present for **myself**.

   (c) My brother and **I** went for a run.

41. Less or fewer? Who or whom?

1 (a) fewer laws   (f) less rain

   (b) less oppression   (g) less clean air

   (c) less money   (h) fewer diseases

   (d) fewer opportunities   (i) less than £50

   (e) less than a mile

2 (a) Children had less chance of a good education.

   (b) Fewer ✓ children went to school.

   (c) Fewer workers were joining the unions.

   (d) There was less ✓ food to go round.

3 (a) Who would like to leave early?

   (b) To whom it may concern.

   (c) The police arrested 50 demonstrators, most of whom were
       later released.

4 (a) To whom should I send my CV?

   (b) With whom did Elizabeth visit Pemberley?

42. Whose or who's? That or which?

1 The following bold words should be circled:

   (a) The local people, **whose** wages were very low, could not
       afford to buy houses in the valley.

   (b) Our uncle, **who's** very sporty, loves to
       go swimming.

   (c) **Who's** got the power to declare war?

   (d) The service is for people **whose** lives have been disrupted by war.

2 (a) The train, **which** doesn't run on Sunday, is free to visitors all
       season.

   (b) The glacier **that** that lies above Chamonix is retreating
       rapidly.

   (c) Football, **which** many of us enjoy, is a very skillful sport.

   (d) This is the film **that** everyone is talking about.

3 (a) Piggy, **whose** real name is never revealed, is the most
       vulnerable member of the group.

   (b) It bounces off the table and hits my headteacher, **who's**
       looking straight at me.

   (c) The mountains **that** are found in the Chamonix valley are the
       highest in the Alps.

   (d) Skiing, **which** is my favourite sport, can be very expensive.

43. Have or of? Effect or affect?

1 (a) Henry VIII could **have** wanted to impress Francis I.

   (b) Richard I's companions might **have** described him as a
       fearless warrior.

2 (a) Research shows that the more sleep you have **affects** your
       exam grades.

   (b) Weather conditions have an **effect** on residents in the south-west.

(c) The beneficial **effects** of drinking water are well-known.

3 (a) I could **have** improved if I **had** known the long-term **effects** of my actions.

(b) An early football injury might **have affected** his mobility.

(c) I should **have** volunteered for the study into the **effects** of revision on exam results.

44. Negatives

1 Suggested answers:

(a) Thomas Sydenham convinced people that a disease **had nothing to do** with the person who had it.

(b) Most Exodusters **did not have any money** for setting up a farm.

(c) The big ranchers **would not share any** of their political power with the newcomers.

2 (a) She **doesn't** want to go to revision club.

(b) Draw clearly, but **don't** worry about creating a work of art!

(c) One advantage of developing wind energy is that it **doesn't** pollute the atmosphere with harmful greenhouse gases.

3 Suggested answers:

(a) Elizabeth's family **does not have** much money so she **cannot** buy **any** fine clothes.

(b) Piggy is intellectual but he **does not have any** common sense.

(c) There **is not** a single member of the family who **is not** implicated in Eva's demise.

45. Active and passive

1 (a) I broke the window.

(b) William ate/has eaten the chocolate.

2 (a) Three letters were/have been delivered this morning.

(b) The test tube was put in the rack.

3 (a) (i) Active (ii) Passive (iii) Passive

(b) (i) The corridors are roamed by unruly students.

(ii) The clamp held the flask filled with water in place.

(iii) Who ate the last cake?

46. Simple present tense

1 a, c, d, f, i and j are in the simple present tense.

2

	to talk	to be	to have
I	talk	am	have
you (singular)	talk	are	have
he/ she/ it	talks	is	has
we	talk	are	have
you (plural)	talk	are	have
they	talk	are	have

3 (a) you are (b) she walks (c) I break

(b) she builds (e) they buy (f) he catches

(g) I creep (h) we drive

47. Present continuous tense

1

Simple present	Present continuous (to be plus -ing)
I write	I am writing
you write (singular)	you are writing
he/she/it writes	he is writing
we write	we are writing
you write (plural)	you are writing
they write	they are writing

2 (b) she **is voting** (c) he **is agreeing** (d) you **are stopping**

3

Simple present	Past continuous (past tense of to be plus –ing)
I read	I was reading
you read (singular)	you were reading
he/she/it reads	he was reading
we read	we were reading
you read (plural)	you were reading
they read	they were reading

4 (a) we **were putting** (b) they **were dancing**

(c) you **were going** (d) we **were saving**

48. Simple past tense

1 (a) added (b) begged (c) filed

(d) played (e) spied (f) hoped

2

Verb...	Rule	Example
ending with two or more consonants.	Add -ed	to land → landed
with a short vowel sound and ending with one consonant.	Double the consonant and add -ed.	to flip → flipped
ending with an 'e'.	Add -d.	to race → raced
ending with a consonant and a 'y'.	Change the 'y' to an 'i' and add -ed.	to pity → pitied
ending with a vowel and 'y'.	Do not change the 'y' to an 'i'. Simply add -ed.	to slay → slayed

3 (a) preferred (b) occurred

(c) emitted (b) labelled

(e) travelled (f) worshipped

(g) kidnapped (h) developed

(i) finished (j) completed

49. Irregular past tense

1

Verb	Simple past	Examples
to be	was or were	1953–1960 was a time of great danger during the Cold War.
to go	went	People went on Crusades because the Church encouraged them.
to take	took	Through the Strength through Joy Movement (KdF), the government took control of the individual.
to see	saw	Ordinary people saw that it was impossible to show disapproval.
to give	gave	The ghosts gave Scrooge insights into the impact of his behaviour on those around him.
to show	showed	They showed him that there was still time to change his behaviour.
to begin	began	Scrooge began his transformation.
to write	wrote	Dickens wrote the novella in 1843
to speak	spoke	Jacob Marley spoke to Scrooge first.
to do	did	Scrooge did transform into a generous human being.

2 Suggested sentences:

(b) I **have worn** my school uniform for five years now.

(c) She **has stolen** my idea

(d) You **have been revising**.

(e) He **has gone** to the library.

50. The future

1 (a) I **am going to complete** my revision timetable.

(b) The size of the school **is going to grow** from 800 students to 1000 students.

2 (a) This **will mean** that switching troops from one front to another quickly will be essential.

(b) Uniting the nation **will require** a single leader.

3 (a) Any from:

This **might/could** mean that switching troops from one front to another quickly might/could be essential.
Uniting the nation **might/could** require a single leader.

(b) These verbs do not express the same certainty as using 'will'.

4 Suggested answer:

I sit / am sitting my Maths exam next Thursday.

51. Modal verbs

1

Possibility	Ability	Necessity
might, may, could, must, will, shall, would	could, can	should, ought to, must, need to, have to

2

Certain	Less certain
will, must, shall, have to, need to	may, might, should, ought to, can, could, would

3 (a) I shall not   (b) I ought not   (c) I may not

4 Suggested answers:

(a) Stalin had two options in 1939: he **could** have maintained the friendship with France or negotiated with Germany.

(b) Meena broke her leg and **should** spend several months in hospital.

(c) The harvest has been poor and there **may** not be enough food to last the winter.

52. Subject–verb agreement

1 (a) Mass **movements are** the downhill **movements** of materials under the influence of gravity.

(b) The **teams are** made up of mixed-age students.

2 The following bold words should be circled:

(a) The River Lugg and the River Wye **have** formed the landscape of Hereford and Worcester.

(b) Onomatopoeia and assonance **create** a sense of the battlefield.

(c) The teacher or a teaching assistant **is** in the classroom at all times.

3 Igneous rock, including granite and basalt, **is** hard and formed of crystals so it **is** resistant to erosion.

4 The following bold words should be circled:

(a) The police **are** concerned about public safety in the area.

(b) The children **go** to the local school.

(c) The army **has** been given the orders.

(d) The football team **is** playing against its bitterest rivals on Sunday.

53. Tense consistency

1 Hippocrates ~~is~~ (was) an Ancient Greek doctor. His ideas and books ~~are~~ (were) very influential well into medieval times and beyond. He ~~dismisses~~ (dismissed) the idea that gods cause disease – he ~~believes~~ (believed) there ~~is~~ (was) a physical reason for illness, which ~~needs~~ (needed) a physical cure.

2 The following bold words should be circled:

(a) The first line **suggests** that Manderley **is** an important place as the narrator **has** 'dreamt' of it 'again'.

(b) Both writers **begin** by trying to encourage their audiences to support the viewpoints they **offer**.

(c) Campaigners for restorative justice programmes **claim** it can reduce reoffending by up to 27%.

3 I don't think ~~I am ever~~ (I have ever been) as scared as when I watched my first scary movie when I ~~am~~ (was) only 7 years old. It ~~is~~ (was) 7 o'clock and it ~~becomes~~ (became) dark outside. My mum was in the same room as me, but she ~~is~~ (was) doing the ironing. I switched on the TV and I ~~am pressing~~ (pressed) play. I ~~watch~~ (watched) in silence, until it ~~got~~ (got) to the very end.

STRUCTURING WRITING

54. Paragraphs

1 (i) (a) The 1830 Indian Removal Act forced Indians in eastern states to move west of the Mississippi River. The US government forced 46 000 eastern Indians to give up their lands in return for new lands west of the Mississippi River. Whites then thought this land was worthless – the 'Great American Desert'. **//** In 1834 the Indian Trade and Intercourse Act set out the frontier between the USA and Indian Territory.

(b) Reason: change of time

(ii) (a) The government needed US citizens to go and live in its new territories in the West. **//** By the 1850s, white Americans wanted to use parts of the lands in the West that had been given to Indians. Reservations were the solution.

(b) Reason: change of topic

(iii) (a) Hard rocks like chalk are often left jutting out in the sea, forming headlands. Soft rocks such as sands are eroded more quickly, forming bays. **//** Cliffs are common coastal features. Cliffs are shaped through weathering and erosion.

(b) Reason: change of topic

(iv) (a) "We have common friends," said Mr Utterson. **//** "Common friends!" echoed Mr Hyde, a little hoarsely. "Who are they?" **//** "Jekyll, for instance," said the lawyer. **//** "He never told you," cried Mr Hyde, with a flush of anger. "I did not think you would have lied." **//** "Come," said Mr Utterson, "that is not fitting language."

(b) Reason: change of person (here the person speaking)

55. Introductions

1 (b) Starting with a rhetorical question that invites the reader to think about their own experiences.

(c) Starting with a bold or controversial statement

(d) Starting with a short, relevant and interesting anecdote

(e) Starting with a relevant quotation.

2

Idea	Example
Start with a vivid description. Use a mix of senses to evoke the setting.	The smell of over-boiled swede and cabbage hit him as he entered the school canteen. A sea of black school blazers met his wary gaze.
Start with interesting dialogue. Use interesting verbs and adverbs to make your reader infer what the characters might be talking about.	"Are you certain?" she asked as she moved silently towards the door. "No. I'm never certain," he whispered. "The dawn will show us the truth."
Start with a sense of mystery, conflict or danger. Leave the reader guessing (the exact setting is not described) and reveal the mystery slowly.	We rely on our senses for survival. But we are not beasts. We have culture. Yet we cannot ignore our instincts. And those instincts mean we always win.

56. Conclusions

1 (a) Answers will vary, but your response should contain vivid vocabulary to make your reader imagine the scene, e.g. *Imagine the worlds you could explore, the knowledge you could gain, all at the touch of a button.*

(b) Answers will vary, but your response should contain a rhetorical question that leaves the reader with something to think about, e.g. *Would you like to wear a tartan pleated skirt every day for five years?*

(c) Answers will vary, but your response should contain a reference back to the actions you have suggested, e.g. *We must act quickly and decisively, or we face inflicting cruelty in the name of entertainment.*

(d) Answers will vary, but your response should contain an imperative (command) form of the verb, e.g. *Do not underestimate our younger generation.*

2 (a) Follow   (b) Avoid   (c) Avoid

    (d) Follow   (e) Avoid   (f) Follow

57. Conjunctions

1 (a)

Purpose	Examples of conjunctions
Adding to and explaining a point	accordingly, also, besides
Illustrating and emphasising a point	to illustrate this, such as, undeniably
Comparing and contrasting	in the same way, likewise, on the contrary
Showing time	formerly, hitherto, following this
Summarising and making judgements	to summarise, in brief, in conclusion

(b) Suggested answers:

Purpose	Examples of conjunctions
Adding and explaining a point	firstly, secondly, thirdly, in addition, furthermore, moreover, similarly, subsequently, as a result, therefore, consequently, hence, thus, so, lastly
Illustrating and emphasising a point	indeed, for example, for instance, in particular, especially, certainly, evidently, undoubtedly, significantly
Comparing and contrasting	but, however, by contrast, yet, although, conversely, notwithstanding, nevertheless, nonetheless, despite, instead, whereas
Showing time	then, next, before, at that time, after, later, meanwhile, previously, at the same time, while, when
Summarising and making judgements	to conclude, in short, in summary

2 **Firstly**, medical staff working with radioactive sources have their exposure limited in a number of ways, **including** their distance from the source, shielding the source and minimising the time they spend in the presence of sources. **Furthermore**, their exposure is closely monitored using dosimeter badges. **Although** some patients may be exposed to a dose of radiation for medical diagnosis or treatment (**for example**, detecting and treating cancer), this is only done when the benefits are greater than the possible harm.

58. Useful essay phrases

1 (a)

Purpose	Examples of useful phrases
Adding and explaining a point	of central concern is, this suggests that,
Explaining further	for this reason, to put it another way,
Illustrating and emphasising a point	this makes it clear that, to say nothing of,
Comparing and contrasting	on the other hand, having said that,
Summarising and making judgements	all things considered, the dominant theme is,

(b) Suggested answers:

Purpose	Examples of useful phrases
Adding and explaining a point	it seems that, this creates the impression that, this creates the effect of, it has been established that, it could be argued that, this could be interpreted as, another key point to remember is, in order to understand,
Explaining further	that is to say, to that end, with this in mind, as a consequence, as a result of this,
Illustrating and emphasising a point	this means that, this is proven/evidenced/illustrated by, this view is supported by, not to mention, not only, but also, as we have seen, in light of the evidence, by the same token,
Comparing and contrasting	on the contrary, that being said, despite this,
Summarising and making judgements	above all, the prevailing attitude was, the least persuasive argument seems to be,

2 **It has been established that** there is not enough ethnic diversity in football coaching in the UK. In 2014, a group of former and current footballers announced that football should aim to employ at least one manager from a BAME background for every five positions in the top league. **This meant that** there needed to be an increase of almost 600% (from 3.4%). **With this in mind,** footballing authorities suggested a number of measures and incentives to increase this figure. **Despite this,** the figure had increased by just 20% in the two years following.

59. Comparisons

1 (a) When the temperature is ~~more cool~~ [*cooler*], more of the Earth is covered in ice. This is called a glacial. When the Earth is warmer [✓], like now, it is called an interglacial.

(b) Because of global warming, extreme weather is ~~frequenter~~ [*more frequent*]: heat extremes are five times more common [✓] than 100 years ago.

(c) Caffeine and chocolate are more likely to lead to headaches [✓] than ~~nutritiouser~~ [*more nutritious*] snacks such as fresh fruit and water.

(d) It is clearly ~~beneficialer~~ [*more beneficial*] to use brownfield sites because they are less damaging [✓] to the environment.

2 (a) tangled   more tangled   most tangled

(b) sad   sadder   saddest

(c) important   more important   most important

(d) far   farther/further   farthest/furthest

3

Adjective	Comparative	Superlative
little	littler/less	littlest/least
much	more	most
good	better	best
many	more	most

60. Clauses

1 The following bold words should be circled:

(a) **Enzymes** are used in industry.

(b) **Cheetahs** are the fastest land animals.

(c) **The contestant** performed the song.

(d) **Gardening** is seasonal work.

(e) **We** are revising hard.

(f) **One of the reactive metals** is zinc.

2 Suggested answers:

(a) In order to obtain a meal, **the heron must watch the water patiently**.

(b) Even though we were exhausted, **we had to finish moving house that day**.

(c) As I reached the top of the mountain, **I breathed a huge sigh of relief**.

(d) Because the platform was so crowded, **I couldn't see that my friend had come to meet me**.

3 (a) Waste water from metal ore mines, which is often highly acidic, contains small amounts of toxic metals.

(b) Israel, whose army grew during the war, was under attack from five enemies.

(c) Some minerals, which cannot be seen, are dissolved in the water and carried along in the flow.

(d) Jane's Aunt Reed, who does not care for Jane, sends her away to boarding school.

(e) River embankments are created by the deposition process, which takes place during flooding.

61. Simple sentences

1 (a) The materials (S) form (V) natural embankments (O).

(b) The bypass plans (S) threaten (V) local biodiversity (O).

(c) Human activity (S) is damaging (V) the river habitats (O).

2 Suggested answers:

(a) Can ellipses create tension in a piece of fiction?

(b) Is this type of river bend called a meander?

3 (a)

Simple sentence	Longer sentence
Gardening was out of the question.	Outside, rain battered the windows, through which he could just make out the autumn leaves as they danced around the garden and settled on the surface of the pond. [simple sentence]
This is active transport.	Cells may need to transport molecules against a concentration gradient or transport molecules that are too big to diffuse through the cell membrane. [simple sentence]
Sea water can kill land plants.	[simple sentence] When the concentration of mineral salts in the soil is higher than that inside the roots, the roots cannot take up water by osmosis.

(b) Suggested answers:

(i) Charity fun runs are open to all and provide you with good exercise, good friendships and good fun. **So why not sign up today?**

(ii) **Our time came**. When we were finally called together, they lined us up and got us into our harnesses; gave us a terrifyingly brief explanation of what to do and had us walking over to the climbing wall.

62. Compound sentences

1 Suggested answers:

(a) I like history **but** Sam likes geography.

(b) The teacher explained the theory **and** made it seem easy.

(c) Water can be obtained from natural lakes **or** (it can be obtained) from reservoirs.

(d) Water can become contaminated **so** it needs to be treated before consumption.

(e) Building on floodplains increases the risk of flooding **yet** (it) is still a common practice.

2 Suggested answer:
Gina noticed that the man ahead of her had stopped **so** she stepped to one side to avoid hitting him as she passed by. She passed him **and** he turned towards her. His face was contorted. Was he smiling **or** (was he) angry? The man's eyes had laughter lines around the edges **yet** Gina felt uncomfortable under his gaze. She tried to look away.

63. Complex sentences

1 Suggested answers:

(b) The only thing that matters, **although some would argue differently**, is winning.

(c) We decided not to go to the beach **once we saw the weather forecast**.

(d) **Unless Mum made us**, we didn't wear our coats.

2 (a) Mitosis is a process **that** causes cells to divide.

(b) The growth of human babies, **which** is regularly checked by measuring them, includes mass and length.

(c) Macbeth, **who** was persuaded to kill Duncan, was tortured by insecurity and guilt.

(d) Lady Macbeth, **whose** ambitions motivated her actions, descended into madness.

3 Suggested answers:

(a) The blunt end of a drumlin faces the direction of ice flow, **whereas** the tapered end points in the direction of glacial flow.

(b) My aunt, **who** was a stern, grey-faced woman, had come to stay.

64. Using quotations

1 (a) The *Guinness Book of World Records* has two entries for what it calls "the world's largest living tree".

(b) The environmentalists called for "a halt to unsustainable tourism", citing "unacceptable levels of noise pollution, litter and erosion" as the main reasons.

(c) Daphne Du Maurier increases the sense of desolation and loneliness by pointing out that "the little lattice windows gaped forlorn".

(d) In *Remember*, Christina Rossetti speaks directly to the reader, repeatedly urging them to "remember me".

(e) It is ironic that, in Act 1, Scene 2, Duncan calls Macbeth "valiant cousin!" and "worthy gentleman!" because Macbeth will betray his respect and trust later in the play.

2 (a) Macbeth suggests that the witches are part of the supernatural world when he states in his letter to Lady Macbeth in Act 1, Scene 5: "I have learned by the perfectest report, they have more in them than mortal knowledge."

(b) The persona's bitter jealously is only made clear towards the end of the poem: "…Oh sir, she smiled, no doubt, / Whene'er I passed her; but who passed without / Much the same smile?"

(c) Jane's outburst finally frees her from the oppressive Reeds: "I am glad you are no relation of mine. I will never call you aunt again as long as I live."

65. Synonyms

1 Suggested answers:

(a) suggest: propose, recommend, intimate

(b) a lot: many, a great deal, plenty

(c) example: specimen, instance, illustration

(d) similarly: likewise, correspondingly, equally

2 (a) The following bold words should be circled:

(i) He **gets lots of money from his job**.

(ii) The King **got** lots of **bad comments** about how he did **his job**.

(iii) The writer **talks about love and stuff** in the poems.

(b) Suggested answers:

(i) He earns a very high salary.

(ii) The king received lots of criticism about his leadership.

(iii) The writer explores the nature of relationships in the poems.

3 Suggested answer:

Fashion is something to talk about and ~~like~~ love with your friends. If all your ~~friends~~ social group ~~like~~ are excited by ~~fashion~~ the latest trends and ~~like~~ love to wear the same ~~fashions~~ styles, then you can swap clothes and tell them if you ~~like~~ are impressed by how they look.

EXAM SKILLS

66. Checking your work

1 Immunisation means making ~~somone~~ someone immune to a ~~disese~~ disease by giving them a ~~vacine~~ vaccine. The ~~vacine~~ vaccine contains an inactive ~~from~~ form of the pathogen that causes the ~~disese~~ disease. As these are not active pathogens, the ~~vacine~~ vaccine will not make the person suffer from the ~~disese~~ disease. // The ~~vacine~~ vaccine contains pathogen antigens. ~~Puting~~ Putting these antigens into a ~~childs~~ child's body causes an ~~imune~~ immune response, which means that lymphocytes that match these ~~particuler~~ particular antigens become activated and produce many matching ~~lymphocyte's~~ lymphocytes and ~~antibodic's~~ antibodies. ~~some~~ Some of the lymphocytes become ~~memry~~ memory lymphocytes and remain in the blood for ~~along~~ a long time. // If the live pathogen gets ^ into the body at a ~~latter~~ later time, the ~~memry~~ memory lymphocytes are already there to ~~reconise~~ recognise the antigens on the pathogen and cause an ~~imune~~ immune response. This response is large ^ and rapid because huge numbers of antibodies ~~is~~ are produced very ~~quickley~~ quickly. The ~~antibodys~~ antibodies attack and kill the pathogens before they can make the child ill.

67. Correcting errors

For vocabulary changes, the answers below are suggestions. Any reasonable suggestion is valid.

1 Public transport is at the heart of a ~~thryving~~ thriving economy. It ~~lets~~ enables people to travel ~~travel~~ to work, to visit cultural attractions and to be ~~apart~~ a part of ^ the local community. // Unfortunately, for those of us who live in remote parts of the country, it can be to very difficult ~~too~~ to integrate with the community because there is a disappointing lack of access to the nearest town. From my ~~place~~ village, there ^ is only one bus each hour to Cottenham and it does not run after 6 o'clock. This means that people in my village are not able to ~~intend~~ attend any evening events or get connecting transport from any other opportunities ~~citys~~ cities, limiting their cultural experiences and employment ~~opportunitys~~ opportunities. // I propose that an hourly service until midnight to ~~to~~ and from Cottenham to its satellite villages should be introduced. My estimate ~~shows~~ suggests that the cost of ~~runnin~~ running the bigger service would be less ~~then~~ than the ^ cost of the annual spring ~~fare~~ fair and would increase spending in Cottenham centre significantly.

68. Improving responses: History

1 Mao launched the 'Anti-Rightist' purge because he wanted to end widespread criticism [spelling] of the Chinese Communist Party **(CCP)** [punctuation]. During the **Hundred Flowers** [capital letters] campaign,[spelling] Mao allowed people to criticise his government. This led economists to criticise the first **Five-Year** Plan,[capital letters] and scientists and experts to criticise the way

the **CCP** [capital letters] ran factories, [punctuation] <u>Students</u> [punctuation] went further and criticised Mao's [punctuation] rule of <u>China</u> [capital letter]. They demanded freedom and de<u>mocra</u>cy, [spelling] which Mao **did** **not** [inappropriate contraction] want to allow. **Therefore**, [conjunction misuse] Mao introduced the 'Anti-Rightist' [punctuation (for consistency with use throughout the answer)] purge to **humiliate** [spelling] and **imprison** [spelling] dangerous **critics** [spelling] of his government. //[paragraph break] **There** [spelling] is also evidence that Mao had planned to launch the 'Anti-Rightist' purge. From 1949, [punctuation] Mao was worried that bureau<u>crats</u> [spelling] were taking over the CCP and that there were still enemies of communism who **had** **not** [inappropriate contraction] been weeded out, [punctuation] Therefore, [punctuation] he launched the 'Anti-Rightist' purge to get rid of bureaucrats and the en<u>e</u>mies [spelling] of the CCP (people who had criticised the government during the Hundred Flowers campaign**)** [punctuation].

2   Answers will vary. Sample answer:

Students went further by criticising Mao's rule of China and demanding freedom and democracy, which Mao did not want to allow.

69. Improving answers: Geography

1   Germany, a developed country, is **investing** [spelling] in finding technolo<u>gies</u> [spelling] to increase the efficiency of wind turbines. After the 2011 <u>Japanese</u> [capital letter] nuclear accidents, Germany**'s** [punctuation] government developed a new plan for increasing renewable energy production. **T**his [punctuation] had a clear focus on offshore wind farms. A second reason for developing sustainable energy resources is that **G**ermany [capital letter] plans to reduce greenhouse gas **emissions** [spelling] by 40 per cent by 2022 to help reduce the impact of **global** **warming**. [inappropriate capital letters] // [paragraph break] China, a developing country, [punctuation] contributes 29 per cent to global carbon emissions – more than any other country. China also has seven of the world's ten most **polluted** [spelling] cities and it burns more coal than the **USA**, [capital letters] Europe and Japan combined. **However**, [misused conjunction] China**'s** [punctuation] <u>Renewable Energy Law</u>, [capital letters] 2006, aims to develop renewable energy resources. China is now a leading **solar** [spelling] power producer. The solar plant being built in the <u>Gobi Desert</u> [capital letters] could produce **energy** [spelling] for one million homes in the future. China's awareness of **its** [punctuation] energy needs has increased <u>take-up</u> [punctuation] of solar panels across the country, [punctuation]

2   Answers will vary. Sample answer:

By 2022, Germany plans to reduce greenhouse gas emissions by 40 per cent. This presents a further driver to develop sustainable energy resources.

70. Improving answers: Religious Studies

1   <u>Christi</u>ans [spelling] have <u>different</u> [spelling] ideas and beliefs about why people suffer and often they question **the purpose of suffering**. [rewritten phrase] Many Christians would agree that it is human beings who do **evil** [spelling] thing**s** [punctuation – no comma needed here] and cause a large amount of <u>suffering</u> [spelling] in the world. For example, every day we see <u>terr</u>orist [spelling] attacks on the television and we also hear of murders and other serious crimes. However, [punctuation] this cannot explain other happenings that could also be seen as evil, such as natural disasters. // [paragraph break] Some Christians <u>believe</u> [spelling] that in some <u>circumstances</u>, [spelling] suffering can lead to **personal** [spelling] growth. These are circumstances when the saying **"**what doesn't kill you makes you

stronger**"** [punctuation] comes into play. Christians also understand that suffering can sometimes bring out the worst in people and can seem a waste of time **to serve no purpose** / **meaningless** [rewritten phrase (suggested answer)]. In some cases, it can lead to a crisis [punctuation] of faith for some Christians, when they begin to doubt their beliefs in the existence of God. // [paragraph break] In the end, [punctuation] Christians accept that there are limits to what human beings can **fully** [spelling] understand or explain about evil and suffering, **They** [punctuation] are comforted in the belief that, because of the suffering <u>experienced</u> [spelling] by Jesus during the <u>cruci</u>fixion [spelling] and during his time on Earth, God can at least understand and relate to human misery and pain, [punctuation]

2   Answers will vary. Sample answer:

Typically, Christians believe that the evil committed by man contributes significantly to the suffering in the world.

71. Improving answers: Biology

1   <u>M</u>itosis [capital letter] is the **cell division** [punctuation] process **that** [wrong word] produces two **d**iploid [inappropriate capital letter] daughter cells from one parent cell. During mit<u>o</u>sis, [spelling] each daughter cell <u>receives</u> [spelling] a copy of <u>every</u> [spelling] chromosome in the parent cell, which means that they are <u>genetically</u> [spelling] identical. **M**itosis [punctuation] is used in asexual reproduction and produces **off**spring [spelling] that are genetically identical to the one parent. [punctuation] // [paragraph break] In m<u>eiosis</u>, [spelling] four <u>daughter</u> [spelling] cells are produced from one <u>parent</u> [spelling] cell. Each daughter cell **is** [subject-verb agreement] haploid and **has** [subject-verb agreement] <u>copies</u> [spelling] of only half the chromosomes of the diploid parent cell. This produces gamete<u>s</u> [punctuation – no comma needed here] that are genetically <u>different</u> [spelling] to each other. Meiosis occurs before **sexual** [wrong word] reproduction, [punctuation] in which two gametes fuse to form a <u>fertilised</u> [spelling] egg cell that is diploid. The <u>variation</u> [spelling] in the gametes means that the offspring <u>differ</u> [spelling] genetically **from** [wrong word] each other and from the two parents, [punctuation]

2   Answers will vary. Sample answer:

Daughter cells are known as 'haploid', which means they possess only half of the normal number of chromosomes.

72. Improving answers: Chemistry

1   **I** [capital letter] think the data show that the reaction in <u>experiment</u> [spelling] 2 is **nine times** [inappropriate abbreviation] faster than the same <u>reaction</u> [spelling] in experiment 1. There are two reasons for the <u>greater</u> [comparative error] rate of reaction in experiment 2. Firstly, [punctuation] the **particles** [spelling] in the powder have a greater surface area than the particles in the **lumps** (or other appropriate word) [wrong word] used in experiment 1. This means that <u>more</u> [comparative error] particles are exposed to the acid **and** [inappropriate abbreviation] **there** [wrong word] are more <u>frequent</u> [spelling] collisions between <u>reactant</u> [spelling] particles, [punctuation] so the rate of reaction is greater. // [paragraph break] **Secondly,** [missing conjunction] the increased rate of reaction is also due to the increased <u>temperature</u> [spelling] of the acid. The reactant particles in <u>experiment</u> 2 [capital letter not needed] have more energy than [wrong word] those in experiment 1. **Therefore,** [capital letter] a greater proportion of them have the activation energy or more. **This** [punctuation] means that the frequency of successful **collis**ions [spelling] is greater, causing a greater rate of reaction. It would **have** [wrong word] been better to vary the size of the particles and the temperature <u>separate</u>ly, [spelling] but the data clearly show that the rate of reaction in experiment 1 is greater than in experiment 2, [punctuation]

Answers

2 Answers will vary. Sample answer:

To ensure a fair test, the two independent variables – particle size and temperature – should have been observed in separate tests, but the results clearly prove the hypothesis.

73. Improving answers: Physics

1 Power is the rate of doing <u>work</u> [spelling] **and** [inappropriate abbreviation] is measured in **watts**. [capital letter not needed] When people climb a hill, they are doing work against <u>gravity</u>, [spelling] and the energy <u>transferred</u> [spelling] is the force (their <u>weight</u>) [spelling] multiplied by the <u>distance</u> [spelling] moved in the direction of the force **(up the hill)**. [punctuation] If the two people **have** [subject-verb agreement] the same weight, as they have both climbed the same distance, [punctuation] in theory **they have** [inappropriate contraction] both transferred the same amount of <u>energy</u>. [spelling] **A**lan [capital letter] exerted **greater** [comparative error] power because he gained the height in a **shorter** [comparative error] time. However, [punctuation] this answer may not be correct if **their** [wrong word] weights are not the same. **It** [capital letter] also <u>assumes</u> [spelling] that the human body is totally **efficient** [spelling], [punctuation] which **it is** [wrong word] not. As **B**ev [capital letter] was walking for longer, [punctuation]she will **waste** [wrong word] more energy and so will **have** [wrong word] transferred more energy altogether. [punctuation]

2 Answers will vary. Sample answer:

However, this conclusion is based on the assumption that both walkers are equal in weight.

74. Improving answers: English Literature

1 Charles <u>Dicken**s's**</u> [punctuation] <u>'A Christmas Carol'</u> [punctuation] is set in <u>**V**ictorian</u> [capital letter] London and depicts a range of issues that <u>**D**ickens</u> [capital letter] personally experienced growing up. It <u>conveys</u> [spelling] a message that was dear to <u>Dicken**s's**</u> [punctuation] heart, namely that of social <u>responsibility</u>. [spelling] Dickens felt very strongly that the inequality in Victorian England was a grave injustice and **sought** [wrong word] to <u>influence</u> [spelling] his <u>readers</u> [punctuation] to change **their** [wrong word] attitudes and behaviour towards **those** [wrong word] less fortunate than themselves. [punctuation] // [paragraph break] In the opening <u>stave</u> [capital letter not needed], [punctuation] Dickens **depicts** [tense] Scrooge as a deeply unpleasant character, [punctuation] almost supernaturally so, and this sets up the <u>atmosphere</u> [spelling] for the rest of the novel. <u>**S**crooge</u> [capital letter] is a "tight-fisted hand" and a **"**squeezing, wrenching, grasping, scraping … old sinner**".** [punctuation] This list of <u>unpleasant</u> [spelling] adjectives <u>immediately</u> [spelling] creates an impression of Scrooge as an <u>aggressive</u> [spelling] and intimidating **character** [spelling]. // [paragraph break] Dickens uses the extended <u>comparison</u> [spelling] of the weather to help the reader recognise just how <u>cold-hearted</u> [punctuation] Scrooge **is**. [tense] 'No wind that blew was bitterer than <u>he</u> [punctuation] …. no pelting rain less open to entreaty." The adjective **'**bitterer**'** [punctuation] gives a strong sense that nothing is more unpleasant to experience than the **presence** [spelling] of Mr Scrooge. [punctuation]

2 Answers will vary. Sample answer:

'A Christmas Carol' draws on Charles Dickens's experiences of growing up in Victorian London to explore a range of issues.

75. Improving answers: English Language

1 Sunlight <u>dappled</u> [tense] on dense foliage and the deep grass below. The sounds of the waves on the coast **were** [wrong word] calm, sweeping across the beach as they <u>oozed</u> [spelling] ~~in and out off~~ **towards** [rewritten phrase (suggested answer)] the shore. Swaying in the gentle <u>breeze</u> [spelling], palms cast shadows across

the <u>white-hot</u> [punctuation] sand. Scattered across the beach, shells <u>beckon**ed**</u> [tense] to the lagoon. This was a **site** [wrong word] of tranquillity; [punctuation] a site of calm. Drifting in the breeze, birdsong flavoured the air.

The silence was <u>shattered</u> [spelling] by the roar from the scarlet creature devouring every inch of the <u>once-beautiful</u> [punctuation] island that got in **its** [wrong word] path. The creeping **snakelike** [one word] vines twisted and <u>slithered</u> [wrong word] around the burning trunks as if brought to life by the fire. Black, now an **omnipresent** [spelling] shade in the sky, <u>transformed</u> [tense] by the plumes of smoke being <u>coughed</u> [spelling] out from the fire, aggressively loomed above. Birds <u>scattered</u> [spelling] from the molten blaze as it destroyed their homes; [punctuation] their helpless <u>cries</u> [spelling] eerie and haunting as they fled the island into the blackened sky.

2 Answers will vary. Sample answer:

The waves sighed gently as they lapped the shore.

Notes

Notes

Notes

Notes

Notes

Published by Pearson Education Limited, 80 Strand, London, WC2R 0RL.

www.pearsonschoolsandfecolleges.co.uk

Text © Pearson Education Limited 2017
Edited, typeset and produced by Elektra Media Ltd
Original illustrations © Pearson Education Limited 2017
Illustrated by Elektra Media Ltd
Cover illustration by Eoin Coveney

The right of Cindy Torn to be identified as author of this work has been asserted by her in accordance with the Copyright, Designs and Patents Act 1988.

First published 2017

20 19 18 17
10 9 8 7 6 5 4 3 2 1

British Library Cataloguing in Publication Data
A catalogue record for this book is available from the British Library

ISBN 9781292211497

Printed in Slovakia by Neografia.